W9-DEW-081

"If any one is sick . . . she appears with her little basket."
[*An Old Maid*]

ADVENTURES IN FRIENDSHIP

ADVENTURES IN FRIENDSHIP

By
DAVID GRAYSON
Author of "Adventures in Contentment"

Illustrated by
THOMAS FOGARTY

NEW YORK
GROSSET & DUNLAP
PUBLISHERS

PUBLISHED, OCTOBER, 1910

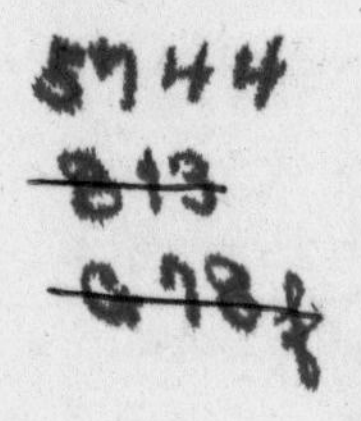

CONTENTS

AN ADVENTURE IN FRATERNITY

I

AN ADVENTURE IN FRATERNITY

THIS, I am firmly convinced, is a strange world, as strange a one as I was ever in. Looking about me I perceive that the simplest things are the most difficult, the plainest things, the darkest, the commonest things, the rarest.

I have had an amusing adventure — and made a friend.

This morning when I went to town for my marketing I met a man who was a Mason, an Oddfellow and an Elk, and who wore the evidences of his various memberships upon his coat. He asked me what lodge

I belonged to, and he slapped me on the back in the heartiest manner, as though he had known me intimately for a long time. (I may say, in passing, that he was trying to sell me a new kind of corn-planter.) I could not help feeling complimented — both complimented and abashed. For I am not a Mason, or an Oddfellow, or an Elk. When I told him so he seemed much surprised and disappointed.

"You ought to belong to one of our lodges," he said. "You'd be sure of having loyal friends wherever you go."

He told me all about his grips and passes and benefits; he told me how much it would cost me to get in and how much more to stay in and how much for a uniform (which was not compulsory). He told me about the fine funeral the Masons would give me; he said that the Elks would care for my widow and children.

"You're just the sort of a man," he said, "that we'd like to have in our lodge. I'd enjoy giving you the grip of fellowship."

He was a rotund, good-humoured man with a shining red nose and a husky voice. He grew so much interested in telling me about his lodges that I think (I *think*) he forgot momentarily that he was selling corn-planters, which was certainly to his credit.

As I drove homeward this afternoon I could not help thinking of the Masons, the Oddfellows and the Elks — and curiously not without a sense of depression. I wondered if my friend of the corn-planters had found the pearl of great price that I have been looking for so long. For is not friendliness the thing of all things that is most pleasant in this world? Sometimes it has seemed to me that the faculty of reaching out and touching one's neighbour where he really lives is the greatest of human achievements. And it was with an indescribable depression that I wondered if these Masons and Oddfellows and Elks had in reality caught the Elusive Secret and confined it within the insurmountable and impenetrable walls of their mysteries, secrets, grips, passes, benefits.

"It must, indeed," I said to myself, "be a precious sort of fraternity that they choose to protect so sedulously."

I felt as though life contained something that I was not permitted to live. I recalled how my friend of the corn-planters had wished to give me the grip of the fellowship — only he could not. I was not entitled to it. I knew no grips or passes. I wore no uniform.

"It is a complicated matter, this fellowship," I said to myself.

So I jogged along feeling rather blue, marveling that those things which often seem so simple should be in reality so difficult.

But on such an afternoon as this no man could possibly remain long depressed. The moment I passed the straggling outskirts of the town and came to the open road, the light and glow of the countryside came in upon me with a newness and sweetness impossible to describe. Looking out across the wide fields I could see the vivid green of the young wheat upon the brown soil; in a distant high pasture the cows had been turned out to the freshening grass; a late pool glistened in the afternoon sunshine. And the crows were calling, and the robins had begun to come: and oh, the moist, cool freshness of the air! In the highest heaven (never so high as at this time of the year) floated a few gauzy clouds: the whole world was busy with spring!

I straightened up in my buggy and drew in a good breath. The mare, half startled, pricked up her ears and began to trot. She, too, felt the spring.

"Here," I said aloud, "is where I belong. I am native to this place; of all these things I am a part."

But presently — how one's mind courses back, like some keen-scented hound, for lost trails — I began to think again of my friend's lodges. And do you know, I had lost every trace of depression. The whole matter lay as clear in my mind, as little complicated, as the countryside which met my eye so openly

"Why!" I exclaimed to myself, "I need not envy my friend's lodges. I myself belong to the greatest of all fraternal orders. I am a member of the Universal Brotherhood of Men."

It came to me so humorously as I sat there in my buggy that I could not help laughing aloud. And I was so deeply absorbed with the idea that I did not at first see the whiskery old man who was coming my way in a farm wagon. He looked at me curiously. As he passed, giving me half the road, I glanced up at him and called out cheerfully:

"How are you, Brother?"

You should have seen him look — and look — and look. After I had passed I glanced back. He had stopped his team, turned half way around in his high seat and was watching me — for he did not understand.

"Yes, my friend," I said to myself, "I *am* intoxicated — with the wine of spring!"

I reflected upon his astonishment when I addressed him as "Brother." A strange word! He did not recognize it. He actually suspected that he was not my Brother.

So I jogged onward thinking about my fraternity, and I don't know when I have had more joy of an idea. It seemed so explanatory!

"I am glad," I said to myself, "that I am a Member. I am sure the Masons have no such benefits to offer in their lodges as we have in ours. And we do not require money of farmers (who have little to pay). We will accept corn, or hen's eggs, or a sandwich at the door, and as for a cheerful glance of the eye, it is for us the best of minted coin."

(Item: to remember. When a man asks money for any good thing, beware of it. You can get a better for nothing.)

I cannot undertake to tell where the amusing reflections which grew out of my idea would finally have led me if I had not been interrupted. Just as I approached the Patterson farm, near the bridge which crosses the creek, I saw a loaded wagon standing on the slope of the hill ahead. The horses seemed to have been unhooked, for the tongue was down, and a man was on his knees between the front wheels.

Involuntarily I said:

"Another member of my society: and in distress!"

I had a heart at that moment for anything. I felt like some old neighbourly Knight travelling the earth in search of adventure. If there had been a distressed mistress handy at that moment, I feel quite certain I could have died for her—if absolutely necessary.

As I drove alongside, the stocky, stout lad of a farmer in his brown duck coat lined with sheep's wool, came up from between the wheels. His cap was awry, his trousers were muddy at the knees where he had knelt in the moist road, and his face was red and angry.

A true knight, I thought to myself, looks not to the beauty of his lady, but only to her distress.

"What's the matter, Brother?" I asked in the friendliest manner.

"Bolt gone," he said gruffly, "and I got to get to town before nightfall."

"Get in," I said, "and we'll drive back. We shall see it in the road."

So he got in. I drove the mare slowly up the hill and we both leaned out and looked. And presently there in the road the bolt lay. My farmer got out and picked it up.

"It's all right," he said. "I was afraid it was clean busted. I'm obliged to you for the lift."

"Hold on," I said, "get in, I'll take you back."

"Oh, I can walk."

"But I can drive you faster," I said

"and you've got to get the load to town before nightfall."

I could not let him go without taking tribute. No matter what the story books say, I am firmly of the opinion that no gentle knight (who was human) ever parted with the fair lady whose misery he had relieved without exchanging the time of day, or offering her a bun from his dinner pail, or finding out (for instance) if she were maid or married.

My farmer laughed and got in.

"You see," I said, "when a member of my society is in distress I always like to help him out."

He paused; I watched him gradually evolve his reply:

"How did you know I was a Mason?"

"Well, I wasn't *sure*."

"I only joined last winter," he said. "I like it first-rate. When you're a Mason you find friends everywhere."

I had some excellent remarks that I could have made at this point, but the distance was short and bolts were irresistibly uppermost. After helping him to put in the bolt, I said:

"Here's the grip of fellowship."

He returned it with a will, but afterward he said doubtfully.

"I didn't feel the grip."

"Didn't you?" I asked. "Well, Brother, it was all there."

"If ever I can do anything for you," he said, "just you let me know. Name's Forbes, Spring Brook."

And so he drove away.

"A real Mason," I said to myself, "could not have had any better advantage of his society at this moment than I. I walked right into it without a grip or a pass. And benefits have also been distributed."

As I drove onward I felt as though anything might happen to me before I got home. I know now exactly how all old knights, all voyageurs, all crusaders, all poets in new places, must have felt! I looked out at every turn of the road; and, finally, after I had grown almost discouraged of encountering further adventure I saw a man walking in the road ahead of me. He was much bent over, and carried on his back a bag.

When he heard me coming he stepped

out of the road and stood silent, saving every unnecessary motion, as a weary man will. He neither looked around nor spoke, but waited for me to go by. He was weary past expectation. I stopped the mare.

"Get in, Brother," I said; "I am going your way."

He looked at me doubtfully; then, as I moved to one side, he let his bag roll off his back into his arms. I could see the swollen veins of his neck; his face had the drawn look of the man who bears burdens.

"Pretty heavy for your buggy," he remarked.

"Heavier for you," I replied.

So he put the bag in the back of my buggy and stepped in beside me diffidently.

"Pull up the lap robe," I said, "and be comfortable."

"Well, sir, I'm glad of a lift," he remarked. "A bag of seed wheat is about all a man wants to carry for four miles."

"Aren't you the man who has taken the old Rucker farm?" I asked.

"I'm that man."

"I've been intending to drop in and see you," I said.

"Have you?" he asked eagerly.

"Yes," I said. "I live just across the hills from you, and I had a notion that we ought to be neighbourly — seeing that we belong to the same society."

His face, which had worn a look of set discouragement (he didn't know beforehand what the Rucker place was like!), had brightened up, but when I spoke of the society it clouded again.

"You must be mistaken," he said. "I'm not a Mason."

"No more am I," I said.

"Nor an Oddfellow."

"Nor I."

As I looked at the man I seemed to know all about him. Some people come to us like that, all at once, opening out to some unsuspected key. His face bore not a few marks of refinement, though work and discouragement had done their best to obliterate them; his nose was thin and high, his eye was blue, too blue, and his chin somehow did not go with the Rucker farm. I knew! A man who in his time had seen many an open door, but who had found them all closed when he attempted to enter! If any one ever needed the benefits of my fraternity, he was that man.

"What Society did you think I belonged to?" he asked.

"Well," I said, "when I was in town a man who wanted to sell me a corn-planter asked me if I was a Mason ——"

"Did he ask you that, too?" interrupted my companion.

"He did," I said. "He did ——" and I reflected not without enthusiasm that I had come away without a corn-planter. "And when I drove out of town I was feeling rather depressed because I wasn't a member of the lodge."

"Were you?" exclaimed my companion. "So was I. I just felt as though I had about reached the last ditch. I haven't any money to pay into lodges and it don't seem's if a man could get acquainted and friendly without."

"Farming is rather lonely work sometimes, isn't it?" I observed.

"You bet it is," he responded. "You've been there yourself, haven't you?"

There may be such a thing as the friendship of prosperity; but surely it cannot be compared with the friendship of adversity. Men, stooping, come close together.

"But when I got to thinking it over," I said, "it suddenly occurred to me that I belonged to the greatest of all fraternities. And I recognized you instantly as a charter member."

He looked around at me expectantly, half laughing. I don't suppose he had so far forgotten his miseries for many a day.

"What's that?" he asked.

"The Universal Brotherhood of Men."

Well, we both laughed — and understood.

After that, what a story he told me! — the story of a misplaced man on an unproductive farm. Is it not marvellous how full people are — all people — of humour, tragedy, passionate human longings, hopes, fears — if only you can unloosen the floodgates! As to my companion, he had been growing bitter and sickly with the pent-up humours of discouragement; all he needed was a listener.

He was so absorbed in his talk that he did not at first realize that we had turned into his own long lane. When he discovered it he exclaimed:

"I didn't mean to bring you out of your way. I can manage the bag all right now."

"Never mind," I said "I want to get you home, to say nothing of hearing how you came out with your pigs."

As we approached the house, a mournful-looking woman came to the door. My companion sprang out of the buggy as much elated now as he had previously been depressed (for that was the coinage of his temperament), rushed up to his wife and led her down to the gate. She was evidently astonished at his enthusiasm. I suppose she thought he had at length discovered his gold mine!

When I finally turned the mare around, he stopped me, laid his hand on my arm and said in a confidential voice:

"I'm glad we discovered that we belong to the same society."

As I drove away I could not help chuckling when I heard his wife ask suspiciously:

"What society is that?"

I heard no word of his answer: only the note in his voice of eager explanation.

And so I drove homeward in the late

twilight, and as I came up the lane, the door of my home opened, the light within gleamed kindly and warmly across the darkened yard: and Harriet was there on the step, waiting.

A DAY OF PLEASANT BREAD

II

A DAY OF PLEASANT BREAD

THEY have all gone now, and the house is very still. For the first time this evening I can hear the familiar sound of the December wind blustering about the house, complaining at closed doorways, asking questions at the shutters; but here in my room, under the green reading lamp, it is warm and still. Although Harriet has closed the doors, covered the coals in the fireplace, and said good-night, the atmosphere still seems to tingle with the electricity of genial humanity.

The parting voice of the Scotch Preacher still booms in my ears:

"This," said he, as he was going out of our door, wrapped like an Arctic highlander in cloaks and tippets, "has been a day of pleasant bread."

One of the very pleasantest I can remember!

I sometimes think we expect too much of Christmas Day. We try to crowd into it the long arrears of kindliness and humanity of the whole year. As for me, I like to take my Christmas a little at a time, all through the year. And thus I drift along into the holidays — let them overtake me unexpectedly — waking up some fine morning and suddenly saying to myself:

"Why, this is Christmas Day!"

How the discovery makes one bound out of his bed! What a new sense of life and adventure it imparts! Almost anything may happen on a day like this — one thinks. I may meet friends I have not seen before in years. Who knows? I may discover that this is a far better and kindlier world than I had ever dreamed it could be.

So I sing out to Harriet as I go down:

"Merry Christmas, Harriet" — and not

waiting for her sleepy reply I go down and build the biggest, warmest, friendliest fire of the year. Then I get into my thick coat and mittens and open the back door. All around the sill, deep on the step, and all about the yard lies the drifted snow: it has transformed my wood pile into a grotesque Indian mound, and it frosts the roof of my barn like a wedding cake. I go at it lustily with my wooden shovel, clearing out a pathway to the gate.

Cold, too; one of the coldest mornings we've had — but clear and very still. The sun is just coming up over the hill near Horace's farm. From Horace's chimney the white wood-smoke of an early fire rises straight upward, all golden with sunshine, into the measureless blue of the sky — on its way to heaven, for aught I know. When I reach the gate my blood is racing warmly in my veins. I straighten my back, thrust my shovel into the snow pile, and shout at the top of my voice, for I can no longer contain myself:

"Merry Christmas, Harriet."

Harriet opens the door — just a crack.

"Merry Christmas yourself, you Arctic explorer! Oo — but it's cold!"

And she closes the door.

Upon hearing these riotous sounds the barnyard suddenly awakens. I hear my horse whinnying from the barn, the chickens begin to crow and cackle, and such a grunting and squealing as the pigs set up from behind the straw stack, it would do a man's heart good to hear!

"It's a friendly world," I say to myself, "and full of business."

I plow through the snow to the stable door. I scuff and stamp the snow away and pull it open with difficulty. A cloud of steam rises out of the warmth within. I step inside. My horse raises his head above the stanchion, looks around at me, and strikes his forefoot on the stable floor — the best greeting he has at his command for a fine Christmas morning. My cow, until now silent, begins to bawl.

I lay my hand on the horse's flank and he steps over in his stall to let me go by. I slap his neck and he lays back his ears playfully. Thus I go out into the passageway and give my horse his oats, throw corn and stalks to the pigs and a handful of grain to Harriet's chickens (it's the only way to stop the cackling!). And thus presently the barnyard is quiet again except for the sound of contented feeding.

Take my word for it, this is one of the pleasant moments of life. I stand and look long at my barnyard family. I observe with satisfaction how plump they are and how well they are bearing the winter. Then I look up at my mountainous straw stack with its capping of snow, and my corn crib with the yellow ears visible through the slats, and my barn with its mow full of hay — all the gatherings of the year, now being expended in growth. I cannot at all explain it, but at such moments the circuit of that dim spiritual battery which each of us conceals within seems to close, and the full current of contentment flows through our lives.

All the morning as I went about my chores I had a peculiar sense of expected pleasure. It seemed certain to me that something unusual and adventurous was about to happen — and if it did not happen offhand, why I was there to make it happen! When I went in to breakfast (do you know the fragrance of broiling bacon when you have worked for an hour before breakfast on a morning of zero weather? If you do not, consider that heaven still has gifts in store for you!) — when I went in to breakfast, I fancied that Harriet looked preoccupied, but I was too busy just then (hot corn muffins) to make an inquiry, and I knew by experience that the best solvent of secrecy is patience.

"David," said Harriet, presently, "the cousins can't come!"

"Can't come!" I exclaimed.

"Why, you act as if you were delighted."

"No — well, yes," I said, "I knew that some extraordinary adventure was about to happen!"

"Adventure! It's a cruel disappointment — I was all ready for them."

"Harriet," I said, "adventure is just what we make it. And aren't we to have the Scotch Preacher and his wife?"

"But I've got such a *good* dinner."

"Well," I said, "there are no two ways about it: it must be eaten! You may depend upon me to do my duty."

"We'll have to send out into the highways and compel them to come in," said Harriet ruefully.

I had several choice observations I should

have liked to make upon this problem, but Harriet was plainly not listening; she sat with her eyes fixed reflectively on the coffee-pot. I watched her for a moment, then I remarked:

"There aren't any."

"David," she exclaimed, "how did you know what I was thinking about?"

"I merely wanted to show you," I said, "that my genius is not properly appreciated in my own household. You thought of highways, didn't you? Then you thought of the poor; especially the poor on Christmas day; then of Mrs. Heney, who isn't poor any more, having married John Daniels; and then I said, 'There aren't any.'"

Harriet laughed.

"It has come to a pretty pass," she said, "when there are no poor people to invite to dinner on Christmas day."

"It's a tragedy, I'll admit," I said, "but let's be logical about it."

"I am willing," said Harriet, "to be as logical as you like."

"Then," I said, "having no poor to invite to dinner we must necessarily try the rich. That's logical, isn't it?"

"Who?" asked Harriet, which is just like a woman. Whenever you get a good healthy argument started with her, she will suddenly short-circuit it, and want to know if you mean Mr. Smith, or Joe Perkins's boys, which I maintain is *not* logical.

"Well, there are the Starkweathers," I said.

"David!"

"They're rich, aren't they?"

"Yes, but you know how they live — what dinners they have — and besides, they probably have a houseful of company."

"Weren't you telling me the other day how many people who were really suffering were too proud to let anyone know about it? Weren't you advising the necessity of getting acquainted with people and finding out — tactfully, of course — you made a point of tact — what the trouble was?"

"But I was talking of *poor* people."

"Why shouldn't a rule that is good for poor people be equally as good for rich people? Aren't they proud?"

"Oh, you can argue," observed Harriet.

"And I can act, too," I said. "I am now going over to invite the Starkweathers. I heard a rumour that their cook has left them and I expect to find them starving in their parlour. Of course they'll be very haughty and proud, but I'll be tactful, and when I go away I'll casually leave a diamond tiara in the front hall."

"What *is* the matter with you this morning?"

"Christmas," I said.

I can't tell how pleased I was with the enterprise I had in mind: it suggested all sorts of amusing and surprising developments. Moreover, I left Harriet, finally, in the breeziest of spirits, having quite forgotten her disappointment over the non-arrival of the cousins.

"If you *should* get the Starkweathers ——"

"'In the bright lexicon of youth,'" I observed, "'there is no such word as fail.'"

So I set off up the town road. A team or two had already been that way and had broken a track through the snow. The sun was now fully up, but the air still tingled with the electricity of zero weather. And the fields! I have seen the fields of June and the fields of October, but I think I never saw our countryside, hills and valleys, tree spaces and brook bottoms, more enchantingly beautiful than it was this morning. Snow everywhere — the fences half hidden, the bridges clogged, the trees laden: where the road was hard it squeaked under my feet, and where it was soft I strode through the drifts. And the air went to one's head like wine!

So I tramped past the Pattersons'. The old man, a grumpy old fellow, was going to the barn with a pail on his arm.

"Merry Christmas," I shouted.

He looked around at me wonderingly and did not reply. At the corners I met the Newton boys so wrapped in tippets that I could see only their eyes and the red ends of their small noses. I passed the Williams's house, where there was a cheerful smoke in the chimney and in the window a green wreath with a lively red bow. And I thought how happy everyone must be on a Christmas morning like this! At the hill bridge who should I meet but the Scotch Preacher himself, God bless him!

"Well, well, David," he exclaimed heartily, "Merry Christmas."

I drew my face down and said solemnly:

"Dr. McAlway, I am on a most serious errand."

"Why, now, what's the matter?" He was all sympathy at once.

"I am out in the highways trying to compel the poor of this neighbourhood to come to our feast."

The Scotch Preacher observed me with a twinkle in his eye.

"David," he said, putting his hand to his mouth as if to speak in my ear, "there is a poor man you will na' have to compel."

"Oh, you don't count," I said. "You're coming anyhow."

Then I told him of the errand with our millionaire friends, into the spirit of which he entered with the greatest zest. He was full of advice and much excited lest I fail to do a thoroughly competent job. For a moment I think he wanted to take the whole thing out of my hands.

"Man, man, it's a lovely thing to do," he exclaimed, "but I ha' me doots — I ha' me doots."

At parting he hesitated a moment, and with a serious face inquired:

"Is it by any chance a goose?"

"It is," I said, "a goose — a big one."

He heaved a sigh of complete satisfaction. "You have comforted my mind," he said, "with the joys of anticipation — a goose, a big goose."

So I left him and went onward toward the Starkweathers'. Presently I saw the great house standing among its wintry trees. There was smoke in the chimney but no other evidence of life. At the gate my spirits, which had been of the best all the morning, began to fail me. Though Harriet and I were well enough acquainted with the Starkweathers, yet at this late moment on Christmas morning it did seem rather a hair-brained scheme to think of inviting them to dinner.

"Never mind," I said, "they'll not be displeased to see me anyway."

I waited in the reception-room, which was cold and felt damp. In the parlour beyond I could see the innumerable things of beauty — furniture, pictures, books, so very, very much of everything — with which the room was filled. I saw it now, as I had often seen it before, with a peculiar sense of weariness. How all these things, though beautiful enough in themselves, must clutter up a man's life!

Do you know, the more I look into life, the more things it seems to me I can successfully lack — and continue to grow happier. How many kinds of food I do not need, nor cooks to cook them, how much curious clothing nor tailors to make it, how many books that I never read, and pictures that are not worth while! The farther I run, the more I feel like casting aside all such impedimenta — lest I fail to arrive at the far goal of my endeavour.

I like to think of an old Japanese nobleman I once read about, who ornamented his house with a single vase at a time, living with it, absorbing its message of beauty, and when he tired of it, replacing it with another. I wonder if he had the right way, and we, with so many objects to hang on our walls, place on our shelves, drape on our chairs, and spread on our floors, have mistaken our course and placed our hearts upon the multiplicity rather than the quality of our possessions!

Presently Mr. Starkweather appeared in the doorway. He wore a velvet smoking-jacket and slippers; and somehow, for a bright morning like this, he seemed old, and worn, and cold.

"Well, well, friend," he said, "I'm glad to see you."

He said it as though he meant it.

"Come into the library; it's the only room in the whole house that is comfortably warm. You've no idea what a task it is to heat a place like this in really cold weather. No sooner do I find a man who can run my furnace than he goes off and leaves me."

"I can sympathize with you," I said, "we often have trouble at our house with the man who builds the fires."

He looked around at me quizzically.

"He lies too long in bed in the morning," I said.

By this time we had arrived at the library, where a bright fire was burning in the grate. It was a fine big room, with dark oak furnishings and books in cases along one wall, but this morning it had a dishevelled and untidy look. On a little table at one side of the fireplace were the remains of a breakfast; at the other a number of wraps were thrown carelessly upon a chair. As I came in Mrs. Starkweather rose from her place, drawing a silk scarf around her shoulders. She is a robust, rather handsome woman, with many rings on her fingers, and a pair of glasses hanging to a little gold hook on her ample bosom; but this morning she, too, looked worried and old.

"Oh, yes," she said with a rueful laugh, "we're beginning a merry Christmas, as you see. Think of Christmas with no cook in the house!"

I felt as if I had discovered a gold mine. Poor starving millionaires!

But Mrs. Starkweather had not told the whole of her sorrowful story.

"We had a company of friends invited for dinner to-day," she said, "and our cook was ill — or said she was — and had to go. One of the maids went with her. The man who looks after the furnace disappeared on Friday, and the stableman has been drinking. We can't very well leave the place without some one who is responsible in charge of it — and so here we are. Merry Christmas!"

I couldn't help laughing. Poor people!

"You might," I said, "apply for Mrs. Heney's place."

"Who is Mrs. Heney?" asked Mrs. Starkweather.

"You don't mean to say that you never heard of Mrs. Heney!" I exclaimed. "Mrs. Heney, who is now Mrs. 'Penny' Daniels? You've missed one of our greatest celebrities."

With that, of course, I had to tell them about Mrs. Heney, who has for years performed a most important function in this community. Alone and unaided she has been the poor whom we are supposed to have always with us. If it had not been for the devoted faithfulness of Mrs. Heney at Thanksgiving, Christmas and other times of the year, I suppose our Woman's Aid Society and the King's Daughters would have perished miserably of undistributed turkeys and tufted comforters. For years Mrs. Heney filled the place most acceptably. Curbing the natural outpourings of a rather jovial soul she could upon occasion look as deserving of charity as any person that ever I met. But I pitied the little Heneys: it always comes hard on the children. For weeks after every Thanksgiving and Christmas they always wore a painfully stuffed and suffocated look. I only came to appreciate fully what a self-sacrificing public servant Mrs. Heney really was when I learned that she had taken the desperate alternative of marrying "Penny" Daniels.

"So you think we might possibly aspire to the position?" laughed Mrs. Starkweather.

Upon this I told them of the trouble in our household and asked them to come down and help us enjoy Dr. McAlway and the goose.

When I left, after much more pleasant talk, they both came with me to the door seeming greatly improved in spirits.

"You've given us something to live for, Mr. Grayson," said Mrs. Starkweather.

So I walked homeward in the highest spirits, and an hour or more later who should we see in the top of our upper field but Mr. Starkweather and his wife floundering in the snow. They reached the lane literally covered from top to toe with snow and both of them ruddy with the cold.

"We walked over," said Mrs. Starkweather breathlessly, "and I haven't had so much fun in years."

Mr. Starkweather helped her over the fence. The Scotch Preacher stood on the steps to receive them, and we all went in together.

I can't pretend to describe Harriet's dinner: the gorgeous brown goose, and the apple sauce, and all the other things that best go with it, and the pumpkin pie at the end — the finest, thickest, most delicious pumpkin pie I ever ate in all my life. It melted in one's mouth and brought visions of celestial bliss. And I wish I could have a picture of Harriet presiding. I have never seen her happier, or more in her element. Every time she brought in a new dish or took off a cover it was a sort of miracle. And her coffee — but I must not and dare not elaborate.

And what great talk we had afterward!

I've known the Scotch Preacher for a long time, but I never saw him in quite such a mood of hilarity. He and Mr. Starkweather told stories of their boyhood — and we laughed, and laughed — Mrs. Starkweather the most of all. Seeing her so often in her carriage, or in the dignity of her home, I didn't think she had so much jollity in her. Finally she discovered Harriet's cabinet organ, and nothing would do but she must sing for us.

"None of the new-fangled ones, Clara," cried her husband: "some of the old ones we used to know."

So she sat herself down at the organ and threw her head back and began to sing:

> "Believe me, if all those endearing young charms,
> Which I gaze on so fondly to-day ——,"

Mr. Starkweather jumped up and ran over to the organ and joined in with his deep voice. Harriet and I followed. The Scotch Preacher's wife nodded in time with the music, and presently I saw the tears in her eyes. As for Dr. McAlway, he sat on the edge of his chair with his hands on his knees and wagged his shaggy head, and before we got through he, too, joined in with his big sonorous voice:

> "Thou wouldst still be adored as this moment thou art——,"

Oh, I can't tell here — it grows late and there's work to-morrow — all the things we did and said. They stayed until it was dark, and when Mrs. Starkweather was ready to go, she took both of Harriet's hands in hers and said with great earnestness:

"I haven't had such a good time at Christmas since I was a little girl. I shall never forget it."

And the dear old Scotch Preacher, when Harriet and I had wrapped him up, went out, saying:

"This has been a day of pleasant bread."

It has; it has. I shall not soon forget it. What a lot of kindness and common human nature — childlike simplicity, if you will — there is in people once you get them down together and persuade them that the things they think serious are not serious at all.

THE OPEN ROAD

III

THE OPEN ROAD

"To make space for wandering is it that the world was made so wide."

—GÖETHE, *Wilhelm Meister.*

I LOVE sometimes to have a day alone — a riotous day. Sometimes I do not care to see even my best friends: but I give myself up to the full enjoyment of the world around me. I go out of my door in the morning — preferably a sunny morning, though any morning will do well enough — and walk straight out into the world. I take with me the burden of no duty or responsibility. I draw in the fresh air, odour-laden from orchard and wood. I look about me as if everything were new — and behold everything *is* new. My barn, my oaks, my fences — I declare I never saw them before. I have no preconceived impressions, or beliefs, or opinions. My lane fence is the end of the known earth. I am a discoverer of new fields among old ones. I see, feel, hear, smell, taste all these wonderful things for the first time. I have no idea what discoveries I shall make!

So I go down the lane, looking up and about me. I cross the town road and climb the fence on the other side. I brush one shoulder among the bushes as I pass: I feel the solid yet easy pressure of the sod. The long blades of the timothy-grass clasp at my legs and let go with reluctance. I break off a twig here and there and taste the tart or bitter sap. I take off my hat and let the warm sun shine on my head. I am an adventurer upon a new earth.

Is it not marvellous how far afield some of us are willing to travel in pursuit of that beauty which we leave behind us at home? We mistake unfamiliarity for beauty; we darken our perceptions with idle foreignness.

For want of that ardent inner curiosity which is the only true foundation for the appreciation of beauty — for beauty is inward, not outward — we find ourselves hastening from land to land, gathering mere curious resemblances which, like unassimilated property, possess no power of fecundation. With what pathetic diligence we collect peaks and passes in Switzerland; how we come laden from England with vain cathedrals!

Beauty? What is it but a new way of approach? For wilderness, for foreignness, I have no need to go a mile: I have only to come up through my thicket or cross my field from my own roadside — and behold, a new heaven and a new earth!

Things grow old and stale, not because they are old, but because we cease to see them. Whole vibrant significant worlds around us disappear within the sombre mists of familiarity. Whichever way we look the roads are dull and barren. There is a tree at our gate we have not seen in years: a flower blooms in our door-yard more wonderful than the shining heights of the Alps!

It has seemed to me sometimes as though I could see men hardening before my eyes, drawing in a feeler here, walling up an opening there. Naming things! Objects fall into categories for them and wear little sure channels in the brain. A mountain is a mountain, a tree a tree to them, a field forever a field. Life solidifies itself in words. And finally how everything wearies them: and that is old age!

Is it not the prime struggle of life to keep the mind plastic? To see and feel and hear things newly? To accept nothing as settled; to defend the eternal right of the questioner? To reject every conclusion of yesterday before the surer observations of to-day? — is not that the best life we know?

And so to the Open Road! Not many miles from my farm there is a tamarack swamp. The soft dark green of it fills the round bowl of a valley. Around it spread rising forests and fields; fences divide it from the known land. Coming across my fields one day, I saw it there. I felt the habit of avoidance. It is a custom, well enough in a practical land, to shun such a spot of perplexity; but on that day I was following the Open Road, and it led me straight to the moist dark stillness of the tamaracks. I cannot here tell all the marvels I found in that place. I trod where human foot had never trod before. Cobwebs barred my passage (the bars to most passages when we came to them are only cobwebs), the earth was soft with the thick swamp mosses, and with many an autumn of fallen dead, brown leaves. I crossed the track of a musk-rat, I saw the nest of a hawk — and how, how many other things of the wilderness I must not here relate. And I came out of it renewed and refreshed; I know now the feeling of the pioneer and the discoverer. Peary has no more than I; Stanley tells me nothing I have not experienced!

What more than that is the accomplishment of the great inventor, poet, painter? Such cannot abide habit-hedged wildernesses. They follow the Open Road, they see for themselves, and will not accept the paths or the names of the world. And Sight, kept clear, becomes, curiously, Insight. A thousand had seen apples fall before Newton. But Newton was dowered with the spirit of the Open Road!

Sometimes as I walk, seeking to see, hear, feel, everything newly, I devise secret words for the things I see: words that convey to me alone the thought, or impression, or emotion of a peculiar spot. All this, I know, to some will seem the acme of foolish illusion. Indeed, I am not telling of it because it is practical; there is no cash at the end of it. I am reporting it as an experience in life; those who understand will understand. And thus out of my journeys I have words which bring back to me with indescribable poignancy the particular impression of a time or a place. I prize them more highly than almost any other of my possessions, for they come to me seemingly out of the air, and the remembrance of them enables me to recall or live over a past experience with scarcely diminished emotion.

And one of these words — how it brings to me the very mood of a gray October day! A sleepy west wind blowing. The fields are bare, the corn shocks brown, and the long road looks flat and dull. Away in the marsh I hear a single melancholy crow. A heavy day, namelessly sad! Old sorrows flock to one's memory and old regrets. The creeper is red in the swamp and the grass is brown on the hill. It comes to me that I was a boy once——

So to the flat road and away! And turn at the turning and rise with the hill. Will the mood change: will the day? I see a lone man in the top of a pasture crying "Coo-ee, coo-ee." I do not see at first why he cries and then over the hill come the ewes, a dense gray flock of them, huddling toward me. The yokel behind has a stick in each hand. "Coo-ee, coo-ee," he also cries. And the two men, gathering in, threatening, sidling, advancing slowly, the sheep turning uncertainly this way and that, come at last to the boarded pen.

"That's the idee," says the helper.

"A poor lot," remarks the leader: "such is the farmer's life."

From the roadway they back their frame-decked wagon to the fence and unhook their team. The leader throws off his coat and stands thick and muscular in his blue jeans — a roistering fellow with a red face, thick neck and chapped hands.

"I'll pass 'em up," he says; "that's a man's work. You stand in the wagon and put 'em in."

So he springs into the yard and the sheep huddle close into the corner, here and there raising a timid head, here and there darting aside in a panic.

"Hi there, it's for you," shouts the leader, and thrusts his hands deep in the wool of one of the ewes.

"Come up here, you Southdown with the bare belly," says the man in the wagon.

"That's my old game — wrastling," the leader remarks, struggling with the next ewe. "Stiddy, stiddy, now I got you, up with you, dang you!"

"That's the idee," says the man in the wagon.

So I watch and they pass up the sheep one by one and as I go on down the road I hear the leader's thick voice, "Stiddy, stiddy," and the response of the other, "That's the idee." And so on into the gray day!

My Open Road leads not only to beauty, not only to fresh adventures in outer observation. I believe in the Open Road in religion, in education, in politics: there is nothing really settled, fenced in, nor finally decided upon this earth. Nothing that is not questionable. I do not mean that I would immediately tear down well-built fences or do away with established and beaten roads. By no means. The wisdom of past ages is likely to be wiser than any hasty conclusions of mine. I would not invite any other person to follow my road until I had well proven it a better way toward truth than that which time had established. And yet I would have every man tread the Open Road; I would have him upon occasion question the smuggest institution and look askance upon the most ancient habit. I would have him throw a doubt upon Newton and defy Darwin! I would have him look straight at men and nature with his own eyes. He should acknowledge no common gods unless he proved them gods for himself. The "equality of men" which we worship: is there not a higher inequality? The material progress which we deify: is it real progress? Democracy — is it after all better than monarchy? I would have him question the canons of art, literature, music, morals: so will he continue young and useful!

And yet sometimes I ask myself. What do I travel for? Why all this excitement and eagerness of inquiry? What is it that I go forth to find? Am I better for keeping my roads open than my neighbour is who travels with contentment the paths of ancient habit? I am gnawed by the tooth of unrest — to what end? Often as I travel I ask myself that question and I have never had a convincing answer. I am looking for something I cannot find. My Open Road is open, too, at the end! What is it that drives a man onward, that scourges him with unanswered questions! We only know that we are driven; we do not know who drives. We travel, we inquire, we look, we work — only knowing that these activities satisfy a certain deep and secret demand within us. We have Faith that there is a Reason: and is there not a present Joy in following the Open Road?

> "And O the joy that is never won,
> But follows and follows the journeying sun."

And at the end of the day the Open Road, if we follow it with wisdom as well as fervour, will bring us safely home again. For after all the Open Road must return to the Beaten Path. The Open Road is for adventure;

and adventure is not the food of life, but the spice.

Thus I came back this evening from rioting in my fields. As I walked down the lane I heard the soft tinkle of a cowbell, a certain earthy exhalation, as of work, came out of the bare fields, the duties of my daily life crowded upon me bringing a pleasant calmness of spirit, and I said to myself:

"Lord be praised for that which is common."

And after I had done my chores I came in, hungry, to my supper.

ON BEING WHERE YOU BELONG

IV

ON BEING WHERE YOU BELONG

Sunday Morning, May 20th.

ON FRIDAY I began planting my corn. For many days previously I went out every morning at sun-up, in the clear, sharp air, and thrust my hand deep down in the soil of the field. I do not know that I followed any learned agricultural rule, but somehow I liked to do it. It has seemed reasonable to me, instead of watching for a phase of the moon (for I do not cultivate the moon), to inquire of the earth itself. For many days I had no response; the soil was of an icy, moist coldness, as of death. "I am not ready yet," it said; "I have not rested my time."

Early in the week we had a day or two of soft sunshine, of fecund warmth, to which the earth lay open, willing, passive. On Thursday morning, though a white frost silvered the harrow ridges, when I thrust my hand into the soil I felt, or seemed to feel, a curious response: a strange answering of life to life. The stone had been rolled from the sepulchre!

And I knew then that the destined time had arrived for my planting. That afternoon I marked out my corn-field, driving the mare to my home-made wooden marker, carefully observant of the straightness of the rows; for a crooked corn-row is a sort of immorality. I brought down my seed corn from the attic, where it had hung waiting all winter, each ear suspended separately by the white, up-turned husks. They were the selected ears of last year's crop, even of size throughout, smooth of kernel, with tips well-covered — the perfect ones chosen among many to perpetuate the highest excellencies of the crop. I carried them to the shed next my barn, and shelled them out in my hand machine: as fine a basket of yellow dent seed as a man ever saw. I have listened to endless discussions as to the relative merits of flint and dent corn. I here cast my vote emphatically for yellow dent: it is the best Nature can do!

I found my seed-bag hanging, dusty, over a rafter in the shed, and Harriet sewed a buckle on the strip that goes around the waist. I cleaned and sharpened my hoe.

"Now," I said to myself, "give me a good day and I am ready to plant."

The sun was just coming up on Friday, looking over the trees into a world of misty and odorous freshness. When I climbed the fence I dropped down in the grass at the far corner of the field. I had looked forward this year with pleasure to the planting of a small field by hand — the adventure of it — after a number of years of horse planting (with Horace's machine) of far larger fields. There is an indescribable satisfaction in answering, "Present!" to the roll-call of Nature: to plant when the earth is ready, to cultivate when the soil begins to bake and harden, to harvest when the grain is fully ripe. It is the chief joy of him who lives close to the soil that he comes, in time, to beat in consonance with the pulse of the earth; its seasons become his seasons; its life his life.

Behold me, then, with a full seed-bag suspended before me, buckled both over the shoulders and around the waist, a shiny hoe in my hand (the scepter of my dominion), a comfortable, rested feeling in every muscle of my body, standing at the end of the first long furrow there in my field on Friday morning — a whole spring day open before me! At that moment I would not have changed my place for the place of any king, prince, or president.

At first I was awkward enough, for it has been a long time since I have done much hand planting; but I soon fell into the rhythmic swing of the sower, the sure, even, accurate step; the turn of the body and the flexing of the wrists as the hoe strikes downward; the deftly hollowed hole; the swing of the hand to the seed-bag; the sure fall of the kernels; the return of the hoe; the final determining pressure of the soil upon the seed. One falls into it and follows it as he would follow the rhythm of a march.

Even the choice of seed becomes automatic, instinctive. At first there is a conscious counting by the fingers — five seeds:

> One for the blackbird,
> One for the crow,
> One for the cutworm,
> Two to grow.

But after a time one ceases to count five, and *feels* five, instinctively rejecting a monstrous six, or returning to complete an inferior four.

I wonder if you know the feel of the fresh, soft soil, as it answers to your steps, giving a little, responding a little (as life always does) — and is there not something endlessly good and pleasant about it? And the movement of the arms and shoulders, falling easily into that action and reaction which yields the most service to the least energy! Scientists tell us that the awkward young eagle has a wider wing-stretch than the old, skilled eagle. So the corn planter, at noon, will do his work with half the expended energy of the early morning: he attains the artistry of motion. And quite beyond and above this physical accomplishment is the ever-present, scarcely conscious sense of reward, repayment, which one experiences as he covers each planting of seeds.

As the sun rose higher the mists stole secretly away, first toward the lower brook-hollows, finally disappearing entirely; the morning coolness passed, the tops of the furrows dried out to a lighter brown, and still I followed the long planting. At each return I refilled my seed-bag, and sometimes I drank from the jug of water which I had hidden in the grass. Often I stood a moment by the fence to look up and around me. Through the clear morning air I could hear the roosters crowing vaingloriously from the barnyard, and the robins were singing, and occasionally from the distant road I heard the rumble of a wagon. I noted the slow kitchen smoke from Horace's chimney, the tip of which I could just see over the hill from the margin of my field — and my own pleasant home among its trees — and my barn — all most satisfying to look upon. Then I returned to the sweat and heat of the open field, and to the steady swing of the sowing.

"OFTEN I STOOD A MOMENT BY THE FENCE"

Joy of life seems to me to arise from a sense of being where one belongs, as I feel right here; of being foursquare with the life we have chosen. All the discontented people I know are trying sedulously to be something they are not, to do something they cannot do. In the advertisements of the county paper I find men angling for money by promising to make women beautiful and men learned or rich — overnight — by inspiring good farmers and carpenters to be poor doctors and lawyers. It is curious, is it not, with what skill we will adapt our sandy land to potatoes and grow our beans in clay, and with how little wisdom we farm the soils of our own natures. We try to grow poetry where plumbing would thrive grandly! — not knowing that plumbing is as important and honourable and necessary to this earth as poetry.

I understand it perfectly; I too, followed long after false gods. I thought I must rush forth to see the world, I must forthwith become great, rich, famous; and I hurried hither and thither, seeking I knew not what. Consuming my days with the infinite distractions of travel, I missed. as one who attempts two occupations at once, the sure satisfaction of either. Beholding the exteriors of cities and of men, I was deceived with shadows; my life took no hold upon that which is deep and true. Colour I got, and form, and a superficial aptitude in judging by symbols. It was like the study of a science: a hasty review gives one the general rules, but it requires a far profounder insight to know the fertile exceptions.

But as I grow older I remain here on my farm, and wait quietly for the world to pass this way. My oak and I, we wait, and we are satisfied. Here we stand among our clods; our feet are rooted deep within the soil. The wind blows upon us and delights us, the rain falls and refreshes us, the sun dries and sweetens us. We are become calm, slow, strong; so we measure rectitudes and regard essentials, my oak and I.

I would be a hard person to dislodge or uproot from this spot of earth. I belong here; I grow here. I like to think of the old fable of the wrestler of Irassa. For I am veritably that Anteus who was the wrestler of Irassa and drew his strength from the ground. So long as I tread the long furrows of my planting, with my feet upon the earth, I am invincible and unconquerable. Hercules himself, though he comes upon me in the guise of Riches, or Fame, or Power, cannot overthrow me — save as he takes me away from this soil. For at each step my strength is renewed. I forget weariness, old age has no dread for me.

Some there may be who think I talk dreams; they do not know reality. My friend, did it ever occur to you that you are unhappy because you have lost connection with life? Because your feet are not somewhere firm planted upon the soil of reality? Contentment, and indeed usefulness, comes as the infallible result of great acceptances, great humilities — of not trying to make ourselves this or that (to conform to some dramatized version of ourselves), but of surrendering ourselves to the fullness of life — of letting life flow through us. To be used! — that is the sublimest thing we know.

It is a distinguishing mark of greatness that it has a tremendous hold upon real things. I have seen men who seemed to have behind them, or rather within them, whole societies, states, institutions: how they come at us, like Atlas bearing the world! For they act not with their own feebleness, but with a strength as of the Whole of Life. They speak, and the words are theirs, but the voice is the Voice of Mankind.

I don't know what to call it: being right with God or right with life. It is strangely the same thing; and God is not particular as to the name we know him by, so long as we know Him. Musing upon these secret things, I seem to understand what the theologians in their darkness have made so obscure. Is it not just this at-one-ment with life which sweetens and saves us all?

In all these writings I have glorified the life of the soil until I am ashamed. I have loved it because it saved me. The farm for me, I decided long ago, is the only place where I can flow strongly and surely. But to you, my friend, life may present a wholly different aspect, variant necessities. Knowing what I have experienced in the city, I have sometimes wondered at the happy (even serene) faces I have seen in crowded streets. There must be, I admit, those who can flow and be at one with that life, too. And let them handle their money, and make shoes, and sew garments, and write in ledgers — if that completes and contents them. I have no quarrel with any one of them. It is, after all, a big and various world, where men can be happy in many ways.

For every man is a magnet, highly and singularly sensitized. Some draw to them fields and woods and hills, and are drawn in return; and some draw swift streets and the riches which are known to cities. It is not of importance what we draw, but that we really draw. And the greatest tragedy in life, as I see it, is that thousands of men and women never have the opportunity to draw with freedom; but they exist in weariness and labour, and are drawn upon like inanimate objects by those who live in unhappy idleness. They do not farm: they are farmed. But that is a question foreign to present considerations. We may be assured, if we draw freely, like the magnet of steel which gathers its iron filings about it in beautiful and symmetrical forms, that the things which we attract will also become symmetrical and harmonious with our lives.

Thus flowing with life, self-surrendering to life, a man becomes indispensable to life;

he is absolutely necessary to the conduct of this universe. And it is the feeling of being necessary, of being desired, flowing into a man that produces the satisfaction of contentment. Often and often I think to myself:

These fields have need of me; my horse whinnies when he hears my step; my dog barks a welcome. These, my neighbours, are glad of me. The corn comes up fresh and green to my planting; my buckwheat bears richly. I am indispensable in this place. What is more satisfactory to the human heart than to be needed and to know we are needed? One line in the Book of Chronicles, when I read it, flies up at me out of the printed page as though it were alive, conveying newly the age-old agony of a misplaced man. After relating the short and evil history of Jehoram, King of Judah, the account ends — with the appalling terseness which often crowns the dramatic climaxes of that matchless writing:

"And (he) departed without being desired."

Without being desired! I have wondered if any man was ever cursed with a more terrible epitaph!

And so I planted my corn; and in the evening I felt the dumb weariness of physical toil. Many times in older days I have known the wakeful nerve-weariness of cities. This was not it. It was the weariness which, after supper, seizes upon one's limbs with half-aching numbness. I sat down on my porch with a nameless content. I looked off across the countryside. I saw the evening shadows fall, and the moon come up. And I wanted nothing I had not. And finally sleep swept in resistless waves upon me and I stumbled up to bed — and sank into dreamless slumber.

THE STORY OF ANNA

V

THE STORY OF ANNA

IT IS the prime secret of the Open Road (but I may here tell it aloud) that you are to pass nothing, reject nothing, despise nothing upon this earth. As you travel, many things both great and small will come to your attention; you are to regard all with open eyes and a heart of simplicity. Believe that everything belongs somewhere; each thing has its fitting and luminous place within this mosaic of human life. The True Road is not open to those who withdraw the skirts of intolerance or lift the chin of pride. Rejecting the least of those who are called common or unclean, it is (curiously) you yourself that you reject. If you despise that which is ugly you do not know that which is beautiful. For what is beauty but completeness? The roadside beggar belongs here, too; and the idiot boy who wanders idly in the open fields; and the girl who withholds (secretly) the name of the father of her child.

I remember as distinctly as though it happened yesterday the particular evening three years ago when I saw the Scotch Preacher come hurrying up the road toward my house. It was June. I had come out after supper to sit on my porch and look out upon the quiet fields. I remember the grateful cool of the evening air, and the scents rising all about me from garden and roadway and orchard. I was tired after the work of the day and sat with a sort of complete comfort and contentment which comes only to those who work long in the quiet of outdoor places. I remember the thought came to me, as it has come in various forms so many times, that in such a big and beautiful world there should be no room for the fever of unhappiness or discontent.

And then I saw McAlway coming up the road. I knew instantly that something was wrong. His step, usually so deliberate, was rapid; there was agitation in every line of his countenance. I walked down through the garden to the gate and met him there. Being somewhat out of breath he did not speak at once. So I said:

"It is not, after all, as bad as you anticipate."

"David," he said, and I think I never heard him speak more seriously, "it is bad enough."

He laid his hand on my arm.

"Can you hitch up your horse and come with me — right away?"

McAlway helped with the buckles and said not a word. In ten minutes, certainly not more, we were driving together down the lane.

"Do you know a family named Williams living on the north road beyond the three corners?" asked the Scotch Preacher.

Instantly a vision of a somewhat dilapidated house, standing not unpicturesquely among ill-kept fields, leaped to my mind.

"Yes," I said; "but I can't remember any of the family except a gingham girl with yellow hair. I used to see her on her way to school."

"A girl!" he said, with a curious note in his voice; "but a woman now."

He paused a moment; then he continued sadly:

"As I grow older it seems a shorter and shorter step between child and child. David, she has a child of her own."

"But I didn't know — she isn't ——"

"A woods child," said the Scotch Preacher.

I could not find a word to say. I remember the hush of the evening there in the country road, the soft light fading in the fields. I heard a whippoorwill calling from the distant woods.

"They made it hard for her," said the Scotch Preacher, "especially her older brother. About four o'clock this afternoon she ran away, taking her baby with her. They found a note saying they would never again see her alive. Her mother says she went toward the river."

I touched up the mare. For a few minutes the Scotch Preacher sat silent, thinking. Then he said, with a peculiar tone of kindness in his voice.

"She was a child, just a child. When I talked with her yesterday she was perfectly docile and apparently contented. I cannot imagine her driven to such a deed of desperation. I asked her: 'Why did you do it, Anna?' She answered, 'I don't know: I — I don't know!' Her reply was not defiant or remorseful: it was merely explanatory."

He remained silent again for a long time.

"David," he said finally, "I sometimes think we don't know half as much about human nature as we — we preach. If we did, I think we'd be more careful in our judgments."

He said it slowly, tentatively: I knew it came straight from his heart. It was this spirit, more than the title he bore, far more than the sermons he preached, that made him in reality the minister of our community. He went about thinking that, after all, he didn't know much, and that therefore he must be kind.

As I drove up to the bridge, the Scotch Preacher put one hand on the reins. I stopped the horse on the embankment and we both stepped out.

"She would undoubtedly have come down this road to the river," McAlway said in a low voice.

It was growing dark. When I walked out on the bridge my legs were strangely unsteady; a weight seemed pressing on my breast so that my breath came hard. We looked down into the shallow, placid water: the calm of the evening was upon it; the middle of the stream was like a rumpled glassy ribbon, but the edges, deep-shaded by overhanging trees, were of a mysterious darkness. In all my life I think I never experienced such a degree of silence — of breathless, oppressive silence. It seemed as if, at any instant, it must burst into some fearful excess of sound.

Suddenly we heard a voice — in half-articulate exclamation. I turned, every nerve strained to the uttermost. A figure, seemingly materialized out of darkness and silence, was moving on the bridge.

"Oh! — McAlway," a voice said.

Then I heard the Scotch Preacher in low tones:

"Have you seen Anna Williams?"

"She is at the house," answered the voice.

"Get your horse," said the Scotch Preacher.

I ran back and led the mare across the bridge (how I remember, in that silence, the thunder of her hoofs on the loose boards!) Just at the top of the little hill leading up from the bridge the two men turned in at a gate. I followed quickly and the three of us entered the house together. I remember the musty, warm, shut-in odour of the front room. I heard the faint cry of a child. The room was dim, with a single kerosene lamp, but I saw three women huddled by the stove, in which a new fire was blazing. Two looked up as we entered, with feminine instinct moving aside to hide the form of the third.

"She's all right, as soon as she gets dry," one of them said.

The other woman turned to us half complainingly:

"She ain't said a single word since we got her in here, and she won't let go of the baby for a minute."

"She don't cry," said the other, "but just sits there like a statue."

McAlway stepped forward and said:

"Well — Anna?"

The girl looked up for the first time. The light shone full in her face: a look I shall never forget. Yes, it was the girl I had seen so often, and yet not the girl. It was the same childish face, but all marked upon with inexplicable wan lines of a certain mysterious womanhood. It was childish, but bearing upon it an inexpressible look of half-sad dignity, that stirred a man's heart to its profoundest depths. And there was in it, too, as I have thought since, a something I have seen in the faces of old, wise men: a light (how shall I explain it?) as of experience — of boundless experience. Her hair hung in wavy dishevelment about her head and shoulders, and she clung passionately to the child in her arms.

The Scotch Preacher had said, "Well — Anna?" She looked up and replied:

"They were going to take my baby away."

"Were they!" exclaimed McAlway in his hearty voice. "Well, we'll never permit *that*. Who's got a better right to the baby than you, I'd like to know?"

Without turning her head, the tears came to her eyes and rolled unheeded down her face.

"Yes, sir, Dr. McAlway," the man said, "I was coming across the bridge with the cows when I see her standing there in the water, her skirts all floating around her. She was hugging the baby up to her face and saying over and over, just like this: 'I don't dare! Oh, I don't dare! But I must. I must.' She was sort of singin' the words: 'I don't dare, I don't dare, but I must.' I jumped the railing and run down to the bank of the river. And I says, 'Come right out o' there'; and she turned and come out just as gentle as a child, and I brought her up here to the house."

It seemed perfectly natural at this time that I should take the girl and her child home to Harriet. She would not go back to her own home, though we tried to persuade her, and the Scotch Preacher's wife was visiting in the city, so she could not go there. But after I found myself driving homeward with the girl — while McAlway went over the hill to tell her family — the mood of action passed. It struck me suddenly, "What will Harriet say?" Upon which my heart sank curiously, and refused to resume its natural position.

In the past I had brought her tramps and peddlers and itinerant preachers, all of whom she had taken in with patience — but this, I knew, was different. For a few minutes I wished devoutly I were in Timbuctu or some other far place. And then the absurdity of the situation struck me all at once, and I couldn't help laughing aloud.

"It's a tremendous old world," I said to myself. "Why, anything may happen anywhere!"

The girl stirred, but did not speak. I was afraid I had frightened her.

"Are you cold?" I asked.

"No, sir," she answered faintly.

I could think of nothing whatever to say, so I said it:

"Are you fond of hot corn-meal mush?"

"Yes, sir," very faintly.

"With cream on it — rich yellow cream — and plenty of sugar?"

"Yes, sir."

"Well, I'll bet a nickel that's what we're going to get!"

"Yes, sir."

We drove up the lane and stopped at the yard gate. Harriet opened the door. I led the small dark figure into the warmth and light of the kitchen. She stood helplessly holding the baby tight in her arms — as forlorn and dishevelled a figure as one could well imagine.

"Harriet," I said, "this is Anna Williams."

Harriet gave me her most tremendous look. It seemed to me at that moment that it wasn't my sister Harriet at all that I was facing, but some stranger and much greater person than I had ever known. Every man has, upon occasion, beheld his wife, his sister, his mother even, become suddenly unknown, suddenly commanding, suddenly greater than himself or any other man. For a woman possesses the occult power of becoming instantly, miraculously, the Accumulated and Personified Customs, Morals and Institutions of the Ages. At this moment, then, I felt myself slowly but surely shrinking and shriveling up. It is a most uncomfortable sensation to find one's self face to face with Society-at-large. Under such circumstances I always know what to do. I run. So I clapped my hat on my head, declared that the mare must be unharnessed immediately, and started for the door. Harriet followed. Once outside she closed the door behind her.

"David, *David*, DAVID," she said.

It occurred to me now for the first time (which shows how stupid I am) that Harriet had already heard the story of Anna Williams. And it had gained so much bulk and robustity in travelling, as such stories do in the country, that I have no doubt the poor child seemed a sort of devastating monster of iniquity. How the country scourges those who do not walk the beaten path! In the careless city such a one may escape to unfamiliar streets and consort with unfamiliar people, and still find a way of life, but here in the country the eye of Society never sleeps!

For a moment I was appalled by what I had done. Then I thought of the Harriet I knew so well: the inexhaustible heart of her. With a sudden inspiration I opened the kitchen door and we both looked in. The girl stood motionless just where I left her: an infinitely pathetic figure.

"Harriet," I said, "that girl is hungry — and cold."

Well, it worked. Instantly Harriet ceased to be Society-at-Large and became the Harriet I know, the Harriet of infinite compassion for all weak creatures. When she had gone in I pulled my hat down and went straight for the barn. I guess I know when it's wise to be absent from places.

I unharnessed the mare, and watered and fed her; I climbed up into the loft and put down a rackful of hay; I let the cows out into the pasture and set up the bars. And then I stood by the gate and looked up into the clear June sky. No man, I think, can remain long silent under the stars, with the brooding, mysterious night around about him, without feeling, poignantly, how little he understands anything, how inconsequential his actions are, how feeble his judgments.

And I thought as I stood there how many a man, deep down in his heart, knows to a certainty that he has escaped being an outcast, not because of any real moral strength or resolution of his own, but because Society has bolstered him up, hedged him about with customs and restrictions until he never has had a really good opportunity to transgress. And some do not sin for very lack of courage and originality: they are helplessly good. How many men in their vanity take to themselves credit for the built-up virtues of men who are dead! There is no cause for surprise when we hear of a "foremost citizen," the "leader in all good works," suddenly gone wrong; not the least cause for surprise. For it was not he that was moral, but Society. Individually he had never been tested, and when the test came he fell. It will give us a large measure of true wisdom if we stop sometimes when we have resisted a temptation and ask ourselves why, at that moment, we did right and not wrong. Was it the deep virtue, the high ideals in our souls, or was it the compulsion of the Society around us? And I think most of us will be astonished to discover what fragile persons we really are — in ourselves.

I stopped for several minutes at the

kitchen door before I dared to go in. Then I stamped vigorously on the boards, as if I had come rushing up to the house without a doubt in my mind — I even whistled — and opened the door jauntily. And had my pains for nothing!

The kitchen was empty, but full of comforting and homelike odours. There was undoubtedly hot mush in the kettle. A few minutes later Harriet came down the stairs. She held up one finger warningly. Her face was transfigured.

"David," she whispered, "the baby's asleep."

So I tiptoed across the room. She tiptoed after me. Then I faced about, and we both stood there on our tiptoes, holding our breath — at least I held mine.

"David," Harriet whispered, "did you see the baby?"

"No," I whispered.

"I think it's the finest baby I ever saw in my life."

When I was a boy, and my great-aunt, who lived for many years in a little room with dormer windows at the top of my father's house, used to tell me stories (the best I ever heard), I was never content with the endings of them. "What happened next?" I remember asking a hundred times; and if I did not ask the question aloud it arose at least in my own mind.

If I were writing fiction I might go on almost indefinitely with the story of Anna; but in real life stories have a curious way of coming to quick fruition, and withering away after having cast the seeds of their immortality.

"Did you see the baby?" Harriet had asked. She said no word about Anna: a BABY had come into the world. Already the present was beginning to draw the charitable curtains of its forgetfulness across this simple drama; already Harriet and Anna and all the rest of us were beginning to look to the "finest baby we ever saw in all our lives."

I might, indeed, go into the character of Anna and the whys and wherefores of her story; but there is curiously little that is strange or unusual about it. It was just Life. A few days with us worked miraculous changes in the girl; like some stray kitten brought in crying from the cold, she curled herself up comfortably there in our home, purring her contentment. She was not in the least a tragic figure: though down deep under the curves and dimples of youth there was something finally resistant, or obstinate, or defiant — which kept its counsel regarding the past.

It is curious how acquaintanceship mitigates our judgments. We classify strangers into whose careers the newspapers or our friends give us glimpses as "bad" or "good"; we separate humanity into inevitable goathood and sheephood. But upon closer acquaintance a man comes to be not bad, but Ebenezer Smith or J. Henry Jones; and a woman is not good, but Nellie Morgan or Mrs. Arthur Cadwalader. Take it in our own cases. Some people, knowing just a little about us, might call us pretty good people; but we know that down in our hearts lurk the possibilities (if not the actual accomplishment) of all sorts of things not at all good. We are exceedingly charitable persons — toward ourselves. And thus we let other people live!

The other day, at Harriet's suggestion, I drove to town by the upper road, passing the Williams place. The old lady has a passion for hollyhocks. A ragged row of them borders the dilapidated picket fence behind which, crowding up to the sociable road, stands the house. As I drive that way it always seems to look out at me like some half-earnest worker, inviting a chat about the weather or the county fair; hence, probably, its good-natured dilapidation. At the gate I heard a voice, and a boy about three years old, in a soiled gingham apron, a sturdy, blue-eyed little chap, whose face was still eloquent of his recent breakfast, came running to meet me. I stopped the mare. A moment later a woman was at the gate between the rows of hollyhocks; when she saw me she began hastily to roll down her sleeves.

"Why, Mr. Grayson!"

"How's the boy, Anna?"

And it was the cheerful talk we had there by the roadside, and the sight of the sturdy boy playing in the sunshine — and the hollyhocks, and the dilapidated house — that brought to memory the old story of Anna which I here set down, not because it carries any moral, but because it is a common little piece out of real life in which Harriet and I have been interested.

THE DRUNKARD

VI

THE DRUNKARD

IT IS a strange thing: Adventure. I looked for her high and I looked for her low, and she passed my door in a tattered garment — unheeded. For I had neither the eye of simplicity nor the heart of humility. One day I looked for her anew and I saw her beckoning from the Open Road; and underneath the tags and tatters I caught the gleam of her celestial garment; and I went with her into a new world.

I have had a singular adventure, in which I have made a friend. And I have seen new things which are also true.

My friend is a drunkard — at least so I call him, following the custom of the country. On his way from town he used often to come by my farm. I could hear him singing afar off. Beginning at the bridge, where on still days one can hear the rattle of a wagon on the loose boards, he sang in a peculiar clear high voice. I make no further comment upon the singing, nor the cause of it; but in the cool of the evening when the air was still — and he usually came in the evening — I often heard the cadences of his song with a thrill of pleasure. Then I saw him come driving by my farm, sitting on the spring seat of his one-horse wagon, and if he chanced to see me in my field, he would take off his hat and make me a grandiloquent bow, but never for a moment stop his singing. And so he passed by the house and I, with a smile, saw him moving up the hill in the north road, until finally his voice, still singing, died away in the distance.

Once I happened to reach the house just as the singer was passing, and Harriet said:

"There goes that drunkard."

It gave me an indescribable shock. Of course I had known as much, and yet I had not directly applied the term. I had not thought of my singer as *that*, for I had often been conscious in spite of myself, alone in my fields, of something human and cheerful which had touched me, in passing.

After Harriet applied her name to my singer, I was of two minds concerning him. I struggled with myself: I tried instinctively to discipline my pulses when I heard the sound of his singing. For was he not a drunkard? Lord! how we get our moralities mixed up with our realities!

And then one evening when I saw him coming — I had been a long day alone in my fields — I experienced a sudden revulsion of feeling. With an indescribable joyousness of adventure I stepped out toward the fence and pretended to be hard at work.

"After all," I said to myself, "this is a large world, with room in it for many curious people."

I waited in excitement. When he came near me I straightened up just as though I had seen him for the first time. When he lifted his hat to me I lifted my hat as grandiloquently as he.

"How are you, neighbour?" I asked.

He paused for a single instant and gave me a smile; then he replaced his hat as though he had far more important business to attend to, and went on up the road.

My next glimpse of him was a complete surprise to me. I saw him on the street in town. Harriet pointed him out, else I should never have recognized him: a quiet, shy, modest man, as different as one could imagine from the singer I had seen so often passing my farm. He wore neat, worn clothes; and his horse stood tied in front of the store. He had brought his honey to town to sell. He was a bee-man.

I stopped and asked him about his honey, and whether the fall flowers had been plenty; I ran my eye over his horse, and said that it seemed to be a good animal. But I could get very little from him, and that little in a rather low voice. I came away with my interest whetted to a still keener edge. How a man has come to be what he

"HE USUALLY CAME IN THE EVENING"

is — is there any discovery better worth making?

After that day in town I watched for the bee-man, and I saw him often on his way to town, silent, somewhat bent forward in his seat, driving his horse with circumspection, a Dr. Jekyll of propriety; and a few hours later he would come homeward a wholly different person, straight of back, joyous of mien, singing his songs in his high clear voice, a very Hyde of recklessness. Even the old horse seemed changed: he held his head higher and stepped with a quicker pace. When the bee-man went toward town he never paused, nor once looked around to see me in my field; but when he came back he watched for me, and when I responded to his bow he would sometimes stop and reply to my greeting.

One day he came from town on foot and when he saw me, even though I was some distance away, he approached the fence and took off his hat, and held out his hand. I walked over toward him. I saw his full face for the first time: a rather handsome face. The hair was thin and curly, the forehead generous and smooth; but the chin was small. His face was slightly flushed and his eyes — his eyes *burned!* I shook his hand.

"I had hoped," I said, "that you would stop sometime as you went by."

"Well, I've wanted to stop — but I'm a busy man. I have important matters in hand almost all the time."

"You usually drive."

"Yes, ordinarily I drive. I do not use a team, but I have in view a fine span of roadsters. One of these days you will see me going by your farm in style. My wife and I both enjoy driving."

I wish I could here convey the tone of buoyancy with which he said these words. There was a largeness and confidence in them that carried me away. He told me that he was now "working with the experts" — those were his words — and that he would soon begin building a house that would astonish the country. Upon this he turned abruptly away, but came back and with fine courtesy shook my hand.

"You see," he said, "I am a busy man, Mr. Grayson — and a happy man."

So he set off down the road, and as he passed my house he began singing again in his high voice. I walked away with a feeling of wonder, not unmixed with sorrow. It was a strange case!

Gradually I became really acquainted with the bee-man, at first with the exuberant, confident, imaginative, home-going bee-man; far more slowly with the shy, reserved, townwardbound bee-man. It was quite an adventure, my first talk with the shy bee-man. I was driving home; I met him near the lower bridge. I cudgeled my brain to think of some way to get at him. As he passed, I leaned out and said:

"Friend, will you do me a favour? I neglected to stop at the post-office. Would you call and see whether anything has been left for me in the box since the carrier started?"

"Certainly," he said, glancing up at me, but turning his head swiftly aside again.

On his way back he stopped and left me a paper. He told me volubly about the way he would run the post-office if he were "in a place of suitable authority."

"Great things are possible," he said, "to the man of ideas."

At this point began one of the by-plays of my acquaintance with the bee-man. The exuberant bee-man referred disparagingly to the shy bee-man.

"I must have looked pretty seedy and stupid this morning on my way in. I was up half the night; but I feel all right now."

The next time I met the shy bee-man he on his part apologised for the exuberant bee-man — hesitatingly, falteringly, winding up with the words, "I think you will understand." I grasped his hand, and left him with a wan smile on his face. Instinctively I came to treat the two men in a wholly different manner. With the one I was blustering, hail-fellow-well-met, listening with eagerness to his expansive talk; but to the other I said little, feeling my way slowly to his friendship, for I could not help looking upon him as a pathetic figure. He needed a friend! The exuberant bee-man was sufficient unto himself, glorious in his visions, and I had from him no little entertainment.

I told Harriet about my adventures: they did not meet with her approval. She said I was encouraging a vice.

"Harriet," I said, "go over and see his wife. I wonder what she thinks about it."

"Thinks!" exclaimed Harriet. "What should the wife of a drunkard think?"

But she went over. As soon as she returned I saw that something was wrong, but I asked no questions. During supper she was extraordinarily preoccupied, and it was not until an hour or more afterward that she came into my room.

"David," she said, "I can't understand some things."

"Isn't human nature doing what it ought to?" I asked.

But she was not to be joked with.

"David, that man's wife doesn't seem to be sorry because he comes home drunken every week or two! I talked with her about it and what do you think she said? She said she knew it was wrong, but she intimated that when he was in that state she loved — liked — him all the better. Is it believable? She said: 'Perhaps you won't understand — it's wrong, I know, but when he comes home that way he seems so full of — life. He — he seems to understand me better then!' She was heartbroken, one could see that, but she would not admit it. I leave it to you, David, what can anyone do with a woman like that? How is the man ever to overcome his habits?"

It is a strange thing, when we ask questions directly of life, how often the answers are unexpected and confusing. Our logic becomes illogical! Our stories won't turn out.

She told much more about her interview: the neat home, the bees in the orchard, the well-kept garden. "When he's sober," she said, "he seems to be a steady, hard worker."

After that I desired more than ever to see deep into the life of the strange bee-man. Why was he what he was?

And at last the time came, as things come to him who desires them faithfully enough. One afternoon not long ago, a fine autumn afternoon, when the trees were glorious on the hills, the Indian summer sun never softer, I was tramping along a wood lane far back of my farm. And at the roadside, near the trunk of an oak tree, sat my friend, the bee-man. He was a picture of despondency, one long hand hanging limp between his knees, his head bowed down. When he saw me he straightened up, looked at me, and settled back again. My heart went out to him, and I sat down beside him.

"Have you ever seen a finer afternoon?" I asked.

He glanced up at the sky.

"Fine?" he answered vaguely, as if it had never occurred to him.

I saw instantly what the matter was; the exuberant bee-man was in process of transformation into the shy bee-man. I don't know exactly how it came about, for such things are difficult to explain, but I led him to talk of himself.

"After it is all over," he said, "of course I am ashamed of myself. You don't know, Mr. Grayson, what it all means. I am ashamed of myself now, and yet I know I shall do it again."

"No," I said," you will not do it again."

"Yes, I shall. Something inside of me argues: Why should you be sorry? Were you not free for a whole afternoon?"

"Free?" I asked.

"Yes — free. You will not understand. But every day I work, work, work. I have friends, but somehow I can't get to them; I can't even get to my wife. It seems as if a wall hemmed me in, as if I were bound to a rock which I couldn't get away from. I am also afraid. When I am sober I know how to do great things, but I can't do them. After a few glasses — I never take more — I not only know I can do great things, but I feel as though I were really doing them."

"But you never do?"

"No, I never do, but I *feel* that I can. All the bonds break and the wall falls down and I am free. I can really touch people. I feel friendly and neighbourly."

He was talking eagerly now, trying to explain, for the first time in his life, he said, how it was that he did what he did. He told me how beautiful it made the world, where before it was miserable and friendless, how he thought of great things and made great plans, how his home seemed finer and better to him, and his work more noble. The man had a real gift of imagination and spoke with an eagerness and eloquence that stirred me deeply. I was almost on the point of asking him where his magic liquor was to be found! When he finally gave me an opening, I said:

"I think I understand. Many men I know are in some respects drunkards. They all want some way to escape themselves — to be free of their own limitations."

"That's it! That's it!" he exclaimed eagerly.

We sat for a time side by side, saying nothing. I could not help thinking of that line of Virgil referring to quite another sort of intoxication:

> "With Voluntary dreams they cheat their minds."

Instead of that beautiful unity of thought and action which marks the finest character, here was this poor tragedy of the divided life. When Fate would destroy a man it first separates his forces! It drives him to think one way and act another; it encourages him to seek through outward stimulation — whether drink, or riches, or fame — a deceptive and unworthy satisfaction in place of that true contentment which comes only from unity within. No man can be two men successfully.

So we sat and said nothing. What indeed can any man *say* to another under such circumstances? As Bobbie Burns remarks out of the depths of his own experience:

> "What's done we partly may compute
> But know not what's resisted."

I've always felt that the best thing one man can give another is the warm hand of understanding. And yet when I thought of the pathetic, shy bee-man, hemmed in by his sunless walls, I felt that I should also say something. Seeing two men struggling shall I not assist the better? Shall I let the sober one be despoiled by him who is riotous? There are realities, but there are also moralities — if we can keep them properly separated.

"Most of us," I said finally, "are in some respects drunkards. We don't give it so harsh a name, but we are just that. Drunkenness is not a mere matter of intoxicating liquors; it goes deeper — far deeper. Drunkenness is the failure of a man to control his thoughts."

The bee-man sat silent, gazing out before him. I noted the blue veins in the hand that lay on his knee. It came over me with sudden amusement and I said:

"I often get drunk myself."

"You?"

"Yes — dreadfully drunk."

He looked at me and laughed — for the first time! And I laughed, too. Do you know, there's a lot of human nature in people! And when you think you are deep in tragedy, behold, humour lurks just around the corner!

"I used to laugh at it a good deal more than I do now," he said. "I've been through it all. Sometimes when I go to town I say to myself, 'I will not turn at that corner,' but when I come to the corner, I do turn. Then I say 'I will not go into that bar,' but I do go in. 'I will not order anything to drink,' I say to myself, and then I hear myself talking aloud to the barkeeper just as though I were some other person. 'Give me a glass of rye,' I say, and I stand off looking at myself, very angry and sorrowful. But gradually I seem to grow weaker and weaker — or rather stronger and stronger — for my brain begins to become clear, and I see things and feel things I never saw or felt before. I want to sing."

"And you do sing," I said.

"I do, indeed," he responded, laughing, "and it seems to me the most beautiful music in the world."

"Sometimes," I said, "when I'm on *my* kind of spree, I try not so much to empty my mind of the thoughts which bother me, but rather to fill my mind with other, stronger thoughts ——"

Before I could finish he had interrupted:

"Haven't I tried that, too? Don't I think of other things? I think of bees — and that leads me to honey, doesn't it? And that makes me think of putting the honey in the wagon and taking it to town. Then, of course, I think how it will sell. Instantly, stronger than you can imagine, I see a dime in my hand. Then it appears on the wet bar. I *smell* the *smell* of the liquor. And there you are!"

We did not talk much more that day. We got up and shook hands and looked each other in the eye. The bee-man turned away, but came back hesitatingly.

"I am glad of this talk, Mr. Grayson. It makes me feel like taking hold again. I have been in hell for years ——"

"Of course," I said. "You needed a friend. You and I will come up together."

As I walked toward home that evening I felt a curious warmth of satisfaction in my soul — and I marvelled at the many strange things that are to be found upon this miraculous earth.

I suppose, if I were writing a story, I should stop at this point; but I am dealing in life. And life does not always respond to our impatience with satisfactory moral conclusions. Life is inconclusive: quite open at the end. I had a vision of a new life for my neighbour, the bee-man — and have it yet, for I have not done with him — but ——

Last evening, and that is why I have been prompted to write the whole story, my bee-man came again along the road by my farm; my exuberant bee-man. I heard him singing afar off.

He did not see me as he went by, but as I stood looking out at him, it came over me with a sudden sense of largeness and quietude that the sun shone on him as genially as it did on me, and that the leaves did not turn aside from him, nor the birds stop singing when he passed.

"He also belongs here," I said.

And I watched him as he mounted the distant hill, until I could no longer hear the high clear cadences of his song. And it seemed to me that something human, in passing, had touched me.

AN OLD MAID

VII

AN OLD MAID

ONE of my neighbours whom I never have chanced to mention before in these writings is a certain Old Maid. She lives about two miles from my farm in a small white house set in the midst of a modest, neat garden with well-kept apple trees in the orchard behind it. She lives all alone save for a good-humoured, stupid nephew who does most of the work on the farm — and does it a little unwillingly. Harriet and I had not been here above a week when we first made the acquaintance of Miss Aiken, or rather she made our acquaintance. For she fills the place, most important in a country community, of a sensitive social tentacle — reaching out to touch with sympathy the stranger. Harriet was amused at first by what she considered an almost unwarrantable curiosity, but we soon formed a genuine liking for the little old lady, and since then we have often seen her in her home, and often she has come to ours.

She was here only last night. I considered her as she sat rocking in front of our fire: a picture of wholesome comfort. I have had much to say of contentment. She seems really to live it, although I have found that contentment is easier to discover in the lives of our neighbours than in our own. All her life long she has lived here in this community, a world of small things, one is tempted to say, with a sort of expected and predictable life. I thought last night, as I observed her gently stirring her rocking-chair, how her life must be made up of small, often-repeated events: pancakes, puddings, patchings, who knows what other orderly, habitual, minute affairs? Who knows? Who knows when he looks at you or at me that there is anything in us beyond the humdrummery of this day?

In front of her house are two long, boarded beds of old-fashioned flowers, mignonette and petunias chiefly, and over the small, very white door with its shiny knob, creeps a white clematis vine. Just inside the hall-door you will discover a bright, clean, oval rag rug, which prepares you, as small things lead to greater, for the larger, brighter, cleaner rug of the sitting-room. There on the centre-table you will discover "Snow Bound," by John Greenleaf Whittier; Tupper's Poems; a large embossed Bible; the family plush album; and a book, with a gilt ladder on the cover which leads upward to gilt stars, called the "Path of Life." On the wall are two companion pictures of a rosy fat child, in faded gilt frames, one called "Wide Awake," the other "Fast Asleep." Not far away, in the corner, on the top of the walnut whatnot, is a curious vase filled with pampas plumes; there are sea-shells and a piece of coral on the shelf below. And right in the midst of the room are three very large black rocking-chairs with cushions in every conceivable and available place — including cushions on the arms. Two of them are for you and me, if we should come in to call; the other is for the cat.

When you sit down you can look out between the starchiest of starchy curtains into the yard, where there is an innumerable busy flock of chickens. She keeps chickens, and all the important ones are named. She has one called Martin Luther, another is Josiah Gilbert Holland. Once she came over to our house with a basket, from one end of which were thrust the sturdy red legs of a pullet. She informed us that she had brought us one of Evangeline's daughters.

But I am getting out of the house before I am fairly well into it. The sitting-room expresses Miss Aiken; but not so well, somehow, as the immaculate bedroom beyond, into which, upon one occasion, I was permitted to steal a modest glimpse. It was of an incomparable neatness and order, all hung about — or so it seemed to me — with white starchy things, and ornamented with bright (but inexpensive) nothings. In this wonderful bedroom there is a secret and sacred drawer into which, once in her life,

Harriet had a glimpse. It contains the clothes, all gently folded, exhaling an odour of lavender, in which our friend will appear when she has closed her eyes to open them no more upon this earth. In such calm readiness she awaits her time.

Upon the bureau in this sacred apartment stands a small rosewood box, which is locked, into which no one in our neighbourhood has had so much as a single peep. I should not dare, of course, to speculate upon its contents; perhaps an old letter or two, "a ring and a rose," a ribbon that is more than a ribbon, a picture that is more than art. Who can tell? As I passed that way I fancied I could distinguish a faint, mysterious odour which I associated with the rosewood box: an old-fashioned odour composed of many simples.

On the stand near the head of the bed and close to the candlestick is a Bible — a little, familiar, daily Bible, very different indeed from the portentous and imposing family Bible which reposes on the centre-table in the front room, which is never opened except to record a death. It has been well worn, this small nightly Bible, by much handling.

Is there a care or a trouble in this world, here is the sure talisman. She seeks (and finds) the inspired text. Wherever she opens the book she seizes the first words her eyes fall upon as a prophetic message to her. Then she goes forth like some David with his sling, so panoplied with courage that she is daunted by no Goliath of the Philistines. Also she has a worshipfulness of all ministers. Sometimes when the Scotch Preacher comes to tea and remarks that her pudding is good, I firmly believe that she interprets the words into a spiritual message for her.

Besides the drawer, the rosewood box, and the worn Bible, there is a certain Black Cape. Far be it from me to attempt a description, but I can say with some assurance that it also occupies a shrine. It may not be in the inner sanctuary, but it certainly occupies a goodly part of the outer porch of the temple. All this, of course, is figurative, for the cape hangs just inside the closet door on a hanger, with a white cloth over the shoulders to keep off the dust. For the vanities of the world enter even such a sanctuary as this. I wish, indeed, that you could see Miss Aiken wearing her cape on a Sunday in the late fall when she comes to church, her sweet old face shining under her black hat, her old-fashioned silk skirt giving out an audible, not unimpressive sound as she moves down the aisle. With what dignity she steps into her pew! With what care she sits down so that she may not crush the cookies in her ample pocket; with what meek pride — if there is such a thing as meek pride — she looks up at the Scotch Preacher as he stands sturdily in his pulpit announcing the first hymn! And many an eye turning that way to look turns with affection.

Several times Harriet and I have been with her to tea. Like many another genius, she has no conception of her own art in such matters as apple puddings. She herself prefers graham gems, in which she believes there inheres a certain mysterious efficacy. She bakes gems on Monday and has them steamed during the remainder of the week — with tea.

And as a sort of dessert she tells us about the Danas, the Aikens and the Carnahans, who are, in various relationships, her progenitors. We gravitate into the other room, and presently she shows us, in the plush album, the portraits of various cousins aunts and uncles. And by-and-by Harriet warms up and begins to tell about the Scribners, the MacIntoshes, and the Strayers, who are *our* progenitors.

"The Aikens," says Miss Aiken, "were always like that — downright and outspoken. It is an Aiken trait. No Aiken could ever help blurting out the truth if he knew he were to die for it the next minute."

"That was like the MacIntoshes," Harriet puts in. "Old Grandfather MacIntosh ——"

By this time I am settled comfortably in the cushioned rocking-chair to watch the fray. Miss Aiken advances a Dana, Harriet counters with a Strayer. Miss Aiken deploys the Carnahans in open order, upon which Harriet entrenches herself with the heroic Scribners and lets fly a MacIntosh who was a general in the colonial army. Surprised, but not defeated, Miss Aiken withdraws in good order, covering her retreat with two *Mayflower* ancestors, the existence of whom she establishes with a blue cup and an ancient silver spoon. No one knows the joy of fighting relatives until he has watched such a battle, following the complete comfort of a good supper.

If any one is sick in the community Miss Aiken hears instantly of it by a sort of wireless telegraphy, or telepathy which would astonish a mystery-loving East Indian. She appears with her little basket, which has two brown flaps for covers opening from the middle and with a spring in them somewhere so that they fly shut with a snap. Out of this she takes a bowl of chicken broth, a jar of ambrosial jelly, a cake of delectable honey and a bottle of celestial raspberry shrub. If the patient will only eat, he will immediately rise up and walk. Or if he dies, it is a pleasant sort of death. I have myself thought on several occasions of being taken with a brief fit of sickness.

In telling all these things about Miss Aiken, which seem to describe her, I have told only the commonplace, the expected or predictable details. Often and often I pause when I see an interesting man or woman and ask myself: "How, after all, does this person live?" For we all know it is not chiefly by the clothes we wear or the house we occupy or the friends we touch. There is something deeper, more secret, which furnishes the real motive and character of our lives. What a triumph, then, is every fine old man! To have come out of a long life with a spirit still sunny, is not that an heroic accomplishment?

Of the real life of our friend I know only one thing; but that thing is precious to me, for it gives me a glimpse of the far dim Alps that rise out of the Plains of Contentment. It is nothing very definite — such things never are; and yet I like to think of it when I see her treading the useful round of her simple life. As I said, she has lived here in this neighbourhood — oh, sixty years. The country knew her father before her. Out of that past, through the dimming eyes of some of the old inhabitants, I have had glimpses of the sprightly girlhood which our friend must have enjoyed. There is even a confused story of a wooer (how people try to account for every old maid!) — a long time ago — who came and went away again. No one remembers much about him — such things are not important, of course, after so many years ——

But I must get to *the* thing I treasure. One day Harriet called at the little house. It was in summer and the door stood open; she presumed on the privilege of friendship and walked straight in. There she saw, sitting at the table, her head on her arm in a curious girlish abandon unlike the prim Miss Aiken we knew so well, our Old Maid. When she heard Harriet's step she started up with breath quickly indrawn. There were tears in her eyes. Something in her hand she concealed in the folds of her skirt then impulsively — unlike her, too — she threw an arm around Harriet and buried her face on Harriet's shoulder. In response to Harriet's question she said:

"Oh, an old, old trouble. No *new* trouble."

That was all there was to it. All the new troubles were the troubles of other people. You may say this isn't much of a clue; well it isn't, and yet I like to have it in mind. It gives me somehow the *other* woman who is not expected or predictable or commonplace. I seem to understand our Old Maid the better; and when I think of her bustling, inquisitive, helpful, gentle ways and the shine of her white soul, I'm sure I don't know what we should do without her in this community.

A ROADSIDE PROPHET

VIII

A ROADSIDE PROPHET

FROM my upper field, when I look across the countryside, I can see in the distance a short stretch of the gray town road. It winds out of a little wood, crosses a knoll, and loses itself again beyond the trees of an old orchard. I love that spot in my upper field, and the view of the road beyond. When I am at work there I have only to look up to see the world go by — part of it going down to the town, and part of it coming up again. And I never see a traveler on the hill, especially if he be afoot, without feeling that if I met him I should like him, and that whatever he had to say I should like to hear.

At first I could not make out what the man was doing. Most of the travellers I see from my field are like the people I commonly meet — so intent upon their destination that they take no joy of the road they travel. They do not even see me here in the fields; and if they did, they would probably think me a slow and unprofitable person. I have nothing that they can carry away and store up in barns, or reduce to percentages, or calculate as profit and loss; they do not perceive what a wonderful place this is; they do not know that here, too, we gather a crop of contentment.

But apparently this man was the pattern of a loiterer. I saw him stop on the knoll and look widely about him. Then he stooped down as though searching for something, then moved slowly forward for a few steps. Just at that point in the road lies a great smooth boulder which road-makers long since dead had rolled out upon the wayside. Here to my astonishment I saw him kneel upon the ground. He had something in one hand with which he seemed intently occupied. After a time he stood up, and retreating a few steps down the road, he scanned the boulder narrowly.

"This," I said to myself, "may be something for me."

So I crossed the fence and walked down the neighbouring field. It was an Indian summer day with hazy hillsides, and still sunshine, and slumbering brown fields — the sort of a day I love. I leaped the little brook in the valley and strode hastily up the opposite slope. I cannot describe what a sense I had of new worlds to be found here in old fields. So I came to the fence on the other side and looked over. My man was kneeling again at the rock. I was scarcely twenty paces from him, but so earnestly was he engaged that he never once saw me. I had a good look at him. He was a small, thin man with straight gray hair; above his collar I could see the weather-brown wrinkles of his neck. His coat was of black, of a noticeably neat appearance, and I observed, as a further evidence of fastidiousness rare upon the Road, that he was saving his trousers by kneeling on a bit of carpet. What he could be doing there so intently by the roadside I could not imagine. So I climbed the fence, making some little intentional noise as I did so. He arose immediately. Then I saw at his side on the ground two small tin cans, and in his hands a pair of paint brushes. As he stepped aside I saw the words he had been painting on the boulder:

GOD IS LOVE

A meek figure, indeed, he looked, and when he saw me advancing he said, with a deference that was almost timidity:

"Good morning, sir."

"Good morning, brother," I returned heartily.

His face brightened perceptibly.

"Don't stop on my account," I said; "finish off your work."

He knelt again on his bit of carpet and proceeded busily with his brushes. I stood and watched him. The lettering was somewhat crude, but he had the swift deftness of long practice.

"How long," I inquired, "have you been at this sort of work?"

"Ten years," he replied, looking up at me with a pale smile. "Off and on for ten years. Winters I work at my trade — I am a journeyman painter — but when spring comes, and again in the fall, I follow the road."

He paused a moment and then said, dropping his voice, in words of the utmost seriousness:

"I live by the Word."

"By the Word?" I asked.

"Yes, by the Word," and putting down his brushes he took from an inner pocket a small package of papers, one of which he handed to me. It bore at the top this sentence in large type:

"Is not my word like fire, saith the Lord: and like a hammer that breaketh the rock in pieces?"

I stood and looked at him a moment. I suppose no one man is stranger than any other, but at that moment it seemed to me I had never met a more curious person. And I was consumed with a desire to know why he was what he was.

"Do you always paint the same sign?" I asked.

"Oh, no," he answered. "I have a feeling about what I should paint. When I came up the road here this morning I stopped a minute, and it all seemed so calm and nice" — he swept his arm in the direction of the fields — "that I says to myself, 'I will paint "God is Love."'"

"An appropriate text," I said, "for this very spot."

He seemed much gratified.

"Oh, you can follow your feelings!" he exclaimed. "Sometimes near towns I can't paint anything but 'Hell yawns,' and 'Prepare to meet thy God.' I don't like 'em as well as 'God is Love,' but it seems like I had to paint 'em. Now, when I was in Arizona ——"

He paused a moment, wiping his brushes.

"When I was in Arizona," he was saying, "mostly I painted 'Repent ye.' It seemed like I couldn't paint anything else, and in some places I felt moved to put 'Repent ye' twice on the same rock."

I began to ask him questions about Arizona, but I soon found how little he, too, had taken toll of the road he travelled: for he seemed to have brought back memories only of the texts he painted and the fact that in some places good stones were scarce, and that he had to carry extra turpentine to thin his paint, the weather being dry. I don't know that he is a lone representative of this trait. I have known farmers who, in travelling, saw only plows and butter-tubs and corn-cribs, and preachers who, looking across such autumn fields as these would carry away only a musty text or two. I pity some of those who expect to go to heaven: they will find so little to surprise them in the golden streets.

But I persevered with my painter, and it was not long before we were talking with the greatest friendliness. Having now finished his work, he shook out his bit of carpet, screwed the tops on his paint cans, wrapped up his brushes, and disposed of them all with the deftness of long experience in his small black bag. Then he stood up and looked critically at his work.

"It's all right," I said; "a great many people coming this way in the next hundred years will see it."

"That's what I want," he said eagerly; "that's what I want. Most people never hear the Word at all."

He paused a moment and then continued:

"It's a curious thing, Mister — perhaps you've noticed it yourself — that the best things of all in the world people won't have as a gift."

"I've noticed it," I said.

"It's strange, isn't it?" he again remarked.

"Very strange," I said.

"I dont know's I can blame them," he continued. "I was that way myself for a good many years: all around me gold and diamonds and precious jewels, and me never once seeing them. All I had to do was to stoop and take them — but I didn't do it."

I saw that I had met a philosopher, and I decided that I would stop and wrestle with him and not let him go without his story — something like Jacob, wasn't it, with the angel?

"Do you do all this without payment?"

He looked at me in an injured way.

"Who'd pay me?" he asked. "Mostly people think me a sort of fool. Oh, I know, but I don't mind. I live by the Word. No, nobody pays me: I am paying myself."

By this time he was ready to start. So I said, "Friend, I'm going your way, and I'll walk with you."

So we set off together down the hill.

"You see, sir," he said, "when a man has got the best thing in the world, and finds it's free, he naturally wants to let other people know about it."

He walked with the unmistakable step of those who knew the long road — an easy, swinging, steady step — carrying his small black bag. So I gradually drew him out, and when I had his whole story it was as simple and common, but as wonderful, as daylight: as fundamental as a tree or a rock.

"You see, Mister," he said, "I was a wild sort when I was young. The drink, and worse. I hear folks say sometimes that if they'd known what was right they'd have done it. But I think that conscience never stops ringing little bells in the back of a man's head; and that if he doesn't do what is right, it's because he *wants* to do what is wrong. He thinks it's more amusing and interesting.

I went through all that, Mister, and plenty more besides. I got pretty nearly as low as a man ever gets. Oh, I was down and out: no home, no family, not a friend that wanted to see me. If you never got down that low, Mister, you don't know what it is. You are just as much dead as if you were in your grave. I'm telling you.

"I thought there was no help for me, and I don't know's I wanted to be helped. I said to myself, 'You're just naturally born weak and it isn't your fault.' It makes a lot of men easier in their minds to lay up their troubles to the way they are born. I made all sorts of excuses for myself, but all the time I knew I was wrong; a man can't fool himself.

"So it went along for years. I got married and we had a little girl."

He paused for a long moment.

"I thought *that* was going to help me. I thought the world and all of that little girl ——" He paused again.

"Well, *she* died. Then I broke my wife's heart and went on down to hell. When a man lets go that way he kills everything he loves and everything that loves him.

He's on the road to loneliness and despair, that man. I'm telling you.

"One day, ten years ago this fall, I was going along the main street in Quinceyville. I was near the end of my rope. Not even money enough to buy drink with, and yet I was then more'n half drunk. I happened to look up on the end of that stone wall near the bridge — were you ever there, Mister? — and I saw the words 'God is Love' painted there. It somehow hit me hard. I couldn't anyways get it out of my mind. 'God is Love.' Well, says I to myself if God is Love, he's the only one that *is* Love for a chap like me. And there's no one else big enough to save me — I says. So I stopped right there in the street, and you may believe it or explain it anyhow you like, Mister, but it seemed to me a kind of light came all around me, and I said, solemn-like, 'I will try God.'"

He stopped a moment. We were walking down the hill: all about us on either side spread the quiet fields. In the high air above a few lacy clouds were drifting eastward. Upon this story of tragic human life crept in pleasantly the calm of the countryside.

"And I did try Him," my companion was saying, "and I found that the words on the wall were true. They were true back there and they've been true ever since. When I began to be decent again and got back my health and my job, I figured that I owed a lot to God. I wa'n't no orator, and no writer and I had no money to give, 'but,' says I to myself, 'I'm a painter. I'll help God with paint.' So here I am a-traveling up and down the roads and mostly painting 'God is Love,' but sometimes 'Repent ye' and 'Hell yawns.' I don't know much about religion — but I do know that His Word is like a fire, and that a man can live by it, and if once a man has it he has everything else he wants."

He paused: I looked around at him again. His face was set steadily ahead — a plain face showing the marks of his hard earlier life, and yet marked with a sort of high beauty.

"The trouble with people who are unhappy, Mister," he said, "is that they won't try God."

I could not answer my companion. There seemed, indeed, nothing more to be said.

All my own speculative incomings and outgoings — how futile they seemed compared with this!

Near the foot of the hill there is a little bridge. It is a pleasant, quiet spot. My companion stopped and put down his bag.

"What do you think," said he, "I should paint here?"

"Well," I said, "you know better than I do. What would *you* paint?"

He looked around at me and then smiled as though he had a quiet little joke with himself.

"When in doubt," he said, "I always paint 'God is Love.' I'm sure of that. Of course 'Hell yawns' and 'Repent ye' have to be painted — near towns — but I much rather paint 'God is Love.'"

I left him kneeling there on the bridge, the bit of carpet under his knees, his two little cans at his side. Half way up the hill I turned to look back. He lifted his hand with the paint brush in it, and I waved mine in return. I have never seen him since, though it will be a long, long time before the sign of him disappears from our roadsides.

At the top of the hill, near the painted

boulder, I climbed the fence, pausing a moment on the top rail to look off across the hazy countryside, warm with the still sweetness of autumn. In the distance, above the crown of a little hill, I could see the roof of my own home — and the barn near it — and the cows feeding quietly in the pastures.

THE GUNSMITH

IX

THE GUNSMITH

HARRIET and I had the first intimation of what we have since called the "gunsmith problem" about ten days ago. It came to us, as was to be expected, from that accomplished spreader of burdens, the Scotch Preacher. When he came in to call on us that evening after supper I could see that he had something important on his mind; but I let him get to it in his own way.

"David," he said finally, "Carlstrom, the gunsmith, is going home to Sweden."

"At last!" I exclaimed.

Dr. McAlway paused a moment and then said hesitatingly:

"He *says* he is going."

Harriet laughed. "Then it's all decided," she said; "he isn't going."

"No," said the Scotch Preacher, "it's not decided — yet."

"Dr. McAlway hasn't made up his mind," I said, "whether Carlstrom is to go or not."

But the Scotch Preacher was in no mood for joking.

"David," he said, "did you ever know anything about the homesickness of the foreigner?"

He paused a moment and then continued, nodding his great shaggy head:

"Man, man, how my old mither greeted for Scotland! I mind how a sprig of heather would bring the tears to her eyes; and for twenty years I dared not whistle "Bonnie Doon" or "Charlie Is My Darling" lest it break her heart. 'Tis a pain you've not had, I'm thinking, Davy."

"We all know the longing for old places and old times," I said.

"No, no, David, it's more than that. It's

the wanting and the longing to see the hills of your own land, and the town where you were born, and the street where you played, and the house ——

He paused, "Ah, well, it's hard for those who have it."

"But I haven't heard Carlstrom refer to Sweden for years," I said. "Is it homesickness, or just old age?"

"There ye have it, Davy; the nail right on the head!" exclaimed the Scotch Preacher. "Is it homesickness, or is he just old and tired?"

With that we fell to talking about Carlstrom, the gunsmith. I have known him pretty nearly ever since I came here, now more than ten years ago — and liked him well, too — but it seemed, as Dr. McAlway talked that evening, as though we were making the acquaintance of quite a new and wonderful person. How dull we all are! How we need such an artist as the Scotch Preacher to mould heroes out of the common human clay around us! It takes a sort of greatness to recognize greatness.

In an hour's time the Scotch Preacher had both Harriet and me much excited, and the upshot of the whole matter was that I promised to call on Carlstrom the next day when I went to town.

I scarcely needed the prompting of the Scotch Preacher, for Carlstrom's gunshop has for years been one of the most interesting places in town for me. I went to it now with a new understanding.

Afar off I began to listen for Carlstrom's hammer, and presently I heard the familiar sounds. There were two or three mellow strokes, and I knew that Carlstrom was making the sparks fly from the red iron. Then the hammer rang, and I knew he was striking down on the cold steel of the anvil. It is a pleasant sound to hear.

Carlstrom's shop is just around the corner from the main street. You may know it by a great weather-beaten wooden gun fastened over the doorway, pointing in the daytime at the sky, and in the night at the stars. A stranger passing that way might wonder at the great gun and possibly say to himself:

"A gunshop! How can a man make a living mending guns in such a peaceful community!"

Such a remark merely shows that he doesn't know Carlstrom, nor the shop, nor *us*.

I tied my horse at the corner and went down

to the shop with a peculiar new interest. I saw as if for the first time the old wheels which have stood weathering so long at one end of the building. I saw under the shed at the other end the wonderful assortment of old iron pipes, kettles, tires, a pump or two, many parts of farm machinery, a broken water wheel, and I don't know what other flotsam of thirty years of diligent mending of the iron works of an entire community. All this, you may say — the disorder of old iron, the cinders which cover part of the yard but do not keep out the tangle of goldenrod and catnip and boneset which at this time of the year grows thick along the neighbouring fences — all this, you say, makes no inviting picture. You are wrong. Where honest work is, there is always that which invites the eye.

I know of few things more inviting than to step up to the wide-open doors and look into the shop. The floor, half of hard worn boards half of cinders, the smoky rafters of the roof, the confusion of implements on the benches, the guns in the corners — how all of these things form the subdued background for the flaming forge and the square chimney above it

At one side of the forge you will see the great dusty bellows and you will hear its stertorous breathing. In front stands the old brown anvil set upon a gnarly maple block. A long sweep made of peeled hickory wood controls the bellows, and as you look in upon this lively and pleasant scene you will see that the grimy hand of Carlstrom himself is upon the hickory sweep. As he draws it down and lets it up again with the peculiar rhythmic swing of long experience — heaping up his fire with a little iron paddle held in the other hand — he hums to himself in a high curious old voice, no words at all, just a tune of contented employment in consonance with the breathing of the bellows and the mounting flames of the forge.

As I stood for a moment in the doorway the other day before Carlstrom saw me, I wished I could picture my friend as the typical blacksmith with the brawny arms, the big chest, the deep voice and all that. But as I looked at him newly, the Scotch Preacher's words still in my ears, he seemed, with his stooping shoulders, his gray beard not very well kept, and his thin gray hair, more than ordinarily small and old.

I remember as distinctly as though it were yesterday the first time Carlstrom really impressed himself upon me. It was in my early blind days at the farm. I had gone to him with a part of a horse-rake which I had broken on one of my stony hills.

"Can you mend it?" I asked.

If I had known him better I should never have asked such a question. I saw, indeed, at the time that I had not said the right thing; but how could I know then that Carlstrom never let any broken thing escape him? A watch, or a gun, or a locomotive — they are all alike to him, if they are broken. I believe he would agree to patch the wrecked chariot of Phaëthon!

A week later I came back to the shop.

"Come in, come in," he said when he saw me.

He turned from his forge, set his hands on his hips and looked at me a moment with feigned seriousness.

"So!" he said. "You have come for your job?"

He softened the "j" in job; his whole speech, indeed, had the engaging inflection of the Scandinavian tongue overlaid upon the English words.

"So," he said, and went to his bench with a quick step and an air of almost childish eagerness. He handed me the parts of my hay-rake without a word. I looked them over carefully.

"I can't see where you mended them," I said.

You should have seen his face brighten with pleasure! He allowed me to admire the work in silence for a moment and then he had it out of my hand, as if I couldn't be trusted with anything so important, and he explained how he had done it. A special tool for his lathe had been found necessary in order to do my work properly. This he had made at his forge, and I suppose it had taken him twice as long to make the special tool as it had to mend the parts of my rake; but when I would have paid him for it he would take nothing save for the mending itself. Nor was this a mere rebuke to a doubter. It had delighted him to do a difficult thing, to show the really great skill he had. Indeed, I think our friendship began right there and was based upon the favour I did in bringing him a job that I thought he couldn't do!

When he saw me the other day in the door of his shop he seemed greatly pleased.

"Come in, come in," he said.

"What is this I hear," I said, "about your going back to Sweden?"

"For forty years," he said, "I've been homesick for Sweden. Now I'm an old man and I'm going home."

"But, Carlstrom," I said, "we can't get along without you. Who's going to keep us mended up?"

"You have Charles Baxter," he said, smiling.

For years there had been a quiet sort of rivalry between Carlstrom and Baxter, though Baxter is in the country and works chiefly in wood.

"But Baxter can't mend a gun or a hay-rake, or a pump, to save his life," I said. "You know that."

The old man seemed greatly pleased: he had the simple vanity which is the right of the true workman. But for answer he merely shook his head.

"I have been here forty years," he said,

"and all the time I have been homesick for Sweden."

I found that several men of the town had been in to see Carlstrom and talked with him of his plans, and even while I was there two other friends came in. The old man was delighted with the interest shown. After I left him I went down the street. It seemed as though everybody had heard of Carlstrom's plans, and here and there I felt that the secret hand of the Scotch Preacher had been at work. At the store where I usually trade the merchant talked about it, and the postmaster when I went in for my mail, and the clerk at the drug store, and the harness-maker. I had known a good deal about Carlstrom in the past, for one learns much of his neighbours in ten years, but it seemed to me that day as though his history stood out as something separate and new and impressive.

When he first came here forty years ago I suppose Carlstrom was not unlike most of the foreigners who immigrate to our shores, fired with faith in a free country. He was poor — as poor as a man could possibly be. For several years he worked on a farm —

hard work, for which, owing to his frail physique, he was not well fitted. But he saved money constantly, and after a time he was able to come to town and open a little shop. He made nearly all of his tools with his own hands, he built his own chimney and forge, he even whittled out the wooden gun which stands for a sign over the door of his shop. He had learned his trade in the careful old-country way. Not only could he mend a gun, but he could make one outright, even to the barrel and the wooden stock. In all the years I have known him he has always had on hand some such work — once I remember, a pistol — which he was turning out at odd times for the very satisfaction it gave him. He could not sell one of his hand-made guns for half as much as it cost him, nor does he seem to want to sell them, preferring rather to have them stand in the corner of his shop where he can look at them. His is the incorruptible spirit of the artist!

What a tremendous power there is in work. Carlstrom worked. He was up early in the morning to work, and he worked in the evening as long as daylight lasted, and once

I found him in his shop in the evening, bending low over his bench with a kerosene lamp in front of him. He was humming his inevitable tune and smoothing off with a fine file the nice curves of a rifle trigger. When he had trouble — and what a lot of it he has had in his time! — he worked; and when he was happy he worked all the harder. All the leisurely ones of the town drifted by, all the children and the fools, and often rested in the doorway of his shop. He made them all welcome: he talked with them, but he never stopped working. Clang, clang, would go his anvil, whish, whish, would respond his bellows, creak, creak, would go the hickory sweep — he was helping the world go round!

All this time, though he had sickness in his family, though his wife died, and then his children one after another until only one now remains, he worked and he saved. He bought a lot and built a house to rent; then he built another house; then he bought the land where his shop stands and rebuilt the shop itself. It was an epic of homely work. He took part in the work of the church and on election days he changed

"THE CHILDREN . . . . OFTEN RESTED IN THE DOORWAY OF HIS SHOP"

his coat, and went to the town hall to vote.

In the years since I have known the old gunsmith and something of the town where he works, I have seen young men, born Americans, with every opportunity and encouragement of a free country, growing up there and going to waste. One day I heard one of them, sitting in front of a store, grumbling about the foreigners who were coming in and taking up the land. The young man thought it should be prevented by law. I said nothing; but I listened and heard from the distance the steady clang, clang, of Carlstrom's hammer upon the anvil.

Ketchell, the store-keeper, told me how Carlstrom had longed and planned and saved to be able to go back once more to the old home he had left. Again and again he had got almost enough money ahead to start, and then there would be an interest payment due, or a death in the family, and the money would all go to the banker, the doctor, or the undertaker.

"Of recent years," said Ketchell, "we thought he'd given up the idea. His friends are all here now, and if he went back, he certainly would be disappointed."

A sort of serenity seemed, indeed, to come upon him: his family lie on the quiet hill, old things and old times have grown distant, and upon that anvil of his before the glowing forge he has beaten out for himself a real place in this community. He has beaten out the respect of a whole town; and from the crude human nature with which he started he has fashioned himself wisdom, and peace of mind, and the ripe humour which sees that God is in his world. There are men I know who read many books, hoping to learn how to be happy; let me commend them to Carlstrom, the gunsmith.

I have often reflected upon the incalculable influence of one man upon a community. The town is better for having stood often looking into the fire of Carlstrom's forge, and seeing his hammer strike. I don't know how many times I have heard men repeat observations gathered in Carlstrom's shop. Only the other day I heard the village school teacher say, when I asked him why he always seemed so merry and had so little fault to find with the world.

"Why," he replied, "as Carlstrom, the gunsmith says, 'when I feel like finding fault I always begin with myself and then I never get any farther.'"

Another of Carlstrom's sayings is current in the country.

"It's a good thing," he says, "when a man knows what he pretends to know."

The more I circulated among my friends, the more I heard of Carlstrom. It is odd that I should have gone all these years knowing Carlstrom, and yet never consciously until last week setting him in his rightful place among the men I know. It makes me wonder what other great souls about me are thus concealing themselves in the guise of familiarity. This stooped gray neighbour of mine whom I have seen so often working in his field that he has almost become a part of the landscape — who can tell what heroisms may be locked away from my vision under his old brown hat?

On Wednesday night Carlstrom was at Dr. McAlway's house — with Charles Baxter, my neighbour Horace, and several others And I had still another view of him.

I think there is always something that

surprises one in finding a familiar figure in a wholly new environment. I was so accustomed to the Carlstrom of the gunshop that I could not at once reconcile myself to the Carlstrom of Dr. McAlway's sitting room. And, indeed, there was a striking change in his appearance. He came dressed in the quaint black coat which he wears at funerals. His hair was brushed straight back from his broad, smooth forehead and his mild blue eyes were bright behind an especially shiny pair of steel-bowed spectacles. He looked more like some old-fashioned college professor than he did like a smith.

The old gunsmith had that pride of humility which is about the best pride in this world. He was perfectly at home at the Scotch Preacher's hearth. Indeed, he radiated a sort of beaming good will; he had a native desire to make everything pleasant. I did not realize before what a fund of humour the old man had. The Scotch Preacher rallied him on the number of houses he now owns, and suggested that he ought to get a wife to keep at least one of them for him. Carlstrom looked around with a twinkle in his eye.

"When I was a poor man," he said, "and carried boxes from Ketchell's store to help build my first shop, I used to wish I had a wheelbarrow. Now I have four. When I had no house to keep my family in, I used to wish that I had one. Now I have four. I have thought sometimes I would like a wife — but I have not dared to wish for one."

The old gunsmith laughed noiselessly, and then from habit, I suppose, began to hum as he does in his shop — stopping instantly, however, when he realized what he was doing.

During the evening the Scotch Preacher got me to one side and said:

"David, we can't let the old man go."

"No, sir," I said, "we can't."

"All he needs, Davy, is cheering up. It's a cold world sometimes to the old."

I suppose the Scotch Preacher was saying the same thing to all the other men of the company.

When we were preparing to go, Dr. McAlway turned to Carlstrom and said:

"How is it, Carlstrom, that you have come to hold such a place in this community?

How is is that you have got ahead so rapidly?"

The old man leaned forward, beaming through his spectacles, and said eagerly:

"It ist America; it ist America."

"No, Carlstrom, no — it is not all America. It is Carlstrom, too. You work, Carlstrom, and you save."

Every day since Wednesday there has been a steady pressure on Carlstrom; not so much said in words, but people stopping in at the shop and passing a good word. But up to Monday morning the gunsmith went forward steadily with his preparations to leave. On Sunday I saw the Scotch Preacher and found him perplexed as to what to do. I don't know yet positively, that he had a hand in it, though I suspect it, but on Monday afternoon Charles Baxter went by my house on his way to town with a broken saw in his buggy. Such is the perversity of rival artists that I don't think Charles Baxter had ever been to Carlstrom with any work. But this morning when I went to town and stopped at Carlstrom's shop I found the gunsmith humming louder than ever.

"Well, Carlstrom, when are we to say good-by?" I asked.

"I'm not going," he said, and taking me by the sleeve he led me over to his bench and showed me a saw he had mended. Now, a broken saw is one of the high tests of the genius of the mender. To put the pieces together so that the blade will be perfectly smooth, so that the teeth match accurately, is an art which few workmen of to-day would even attempt.

"Charles Baxter brought it in," answered the old gunsmith, unable to conceal his delight. "He thought I couldn't mend it!"

To the true artist there is nothing to equal the approbation of a rival. It was Charles Baxter, I am convinced, who was the deciding factor. Carlstrom couldn't leave with one of Baxter's saws unmended! But back of it all, I know, is the hand and the heart of the Scotch Preacher.

The more I think of it the more I think that our gunsmith possesses many of the qualities of true greatness. He has the serenity, and the humour, and the humility of greatness. He has a real faith in God. He works, he accepts what comes. He thinks there is no more honourable calling than that of gunsmith, and that the town he lives in is the best of all towns, and the people he knows the best people.

Yes, it *is* greatness.

THE MOWING

X

THE MOWING

"Now I see the secret of the making of the best persons,
It is to grow in the open air and to eat and sleep with the earth."

THIS is a well earned Sunday morning. My chores were all done long ago, and I am sitting down here after a late and leisurely breakfast with that luxurious feeling of irresponsible restfulness and comfort which comes only upon a clean, still Sunday morning like this — after a week of hard work — a clean Sunday morning, with clean clothes, and a clean chin, and clean thoughts, and the June airs stirring the clean white curtains at my windows. From across the hills I can hear very faintly the drowsy sounds of early church bells, never indeed to be heard here except on a morning of surpassing tranquillity. And in the barn-yard back of the house Harriet's hens are cackling triumphantly: they are impiously unobservant of the Sabbath day.

I turned out my mare for a run in the pasture. She has rolled herself again and again in the warm earth and shaken herself after each roll with an equine delight most pleasant to see. Now, from time to time, I can hear her gossipy whickerings as she calls across the fields to my neighbour Horace's young bay colts.

When I first woke up this morning I said to myself:

"Well, nothing happened yesterday."

Then I lay quiet for some time — it being Sunday morning — and I turned over in my mind all that I had heard or seen or felt or thought about in that one day. And presently I said aloud to myself:

"Why, nearly everything happened yesterday."

And the more I thought of it the more interesting, the more wonderful, the more explanatory of high things, appeared the common doings of that June Saturday. I had walked among unusual events — and had not known the wonder of them! I had eyes, but I did not see — and ears, but I heard not. It may be, it *may* be, that the Future Life of which we have had such confusing but wistful prophecies is only the reliving with a full understanding, of this marvellous Life that we now know. To a full understanding this day, this moment even — here in this quiet room — would contain enough to crowd an eternity. Oh, we are children yet — playing with things much too large for us — much too full of meaning.

Yesterday I cut my field of early clover. I should have been at it a full week earlier if it had not been for the frequent and sousing spring showers. Already half the blossoms of the clover had turned brown and were shriveling away into inconspicuous seediness. The leaves underneath on the lower parts of the stems were curling up and fading;

many of them had already dropped away. There is a tide also in the affairs of clover and if a farmer would profit by his crop, it must be taken at its flood.

I began to watch the skies with some anxiety, and on Thursday I was delighted to see the weather become clearer, and a warm dry wind spring up from the southwest. On Friday there was not so much as a cloud of the size of a man's hand to be seen anywhere in the sky, not one, and the sun with lively diligence had begun to make up for the listlessness of the past week. It was hot and dry enough to suit the most exacting hay-maker.

Encouraged by these favourable symptoms I sent word to Dick Sheridan (by one of Horace's men) to come over bright and early on Saturday morning. My field is only a small one and so rough and uneven that I had concluded with Dick's help to cut it by hand. I thought that on a pinch it could all be done in one day.

"Harriet," I said, "we'll cut the clover to-morrow."

"That's fortunate," said Harriet, "I'd already arranged to have Ann Spencer in to help me."

Yesterday morning, then, I got out earlier than usual. It was a perfect June morning, one of the brightest and clearest I think I ever saw. The mists had not yet risen from the hollows of my lower fields, and all the earth was fresh with dew and sweet with the mingled odours of growing things. No hour of the whole day is more perfect than this.

I walked out along the edge of the orchard and climbed the fence of the field beyond. As I stooped over I could smell the heavy sweet odour of the clover blossoms. I could see the billowy green sweep of the glistening leaves. I lifted up a mass of the tangled stems and laid the palm of my hand on the earth underneath. It was neither too wet nor too dry.

"We shall have good cutting to-day," I said to myself.

So I stood up and looked with a satisfaction impossible to describe across the acres of my small domain, marking where in the low spots the crop seemed heaviest, where it was lodged and tangled by the wind and the rain, and where in the higher spaces it grew scarce thick enough to cover the sad baldness of the knolls. How much more we get out of life than we deserve!

So I walked along the edge of the field to the orchard gate, which I opened wide.

"Here," I said, "is where we will begin."

So I turned back to the barn. I had not reached the other side of the orchard when who should I see but Dick Sheridan himself, coming in at the lane gate. He had an old, coarse-woven straw hat stuck resplendently on the back of his head. He was carrying his scythe jauntily over his shoulder and whistling "Good-bye, Susan" at the top of his capacity.

Dick Sheridan is a cheerful young fellow with a thin brown face and (milky) blue eyes. He has an enormous Adam's apple which has an odd way of moving up and down when he talks — and one large tooth out in front. His body is like a bundle of wires, as thin and muscular and enduring as that of a broncho pony. He can work all day long and then go down to the lodge-hall at the Crossing and dance half the night. You should really see him when he dances! He can jump straight up and click his heels twice together before he comes down again!

On such occasions he is marvellously clad, as befits the gallant that he really is, but this morning he wore a faded shirt and one of his suspender cords behind was fastened with a nail instead of a button. His socks are sometimes pale blue and sometimes lavender and commonly, therefore, he turns up his trouser legs so that these vanities may not be wholly lost upon a dull world. His full name is Richard Tecumseh Sheridan, but every one calls him Dick. A good, cheerful fellow, Dick, and a hard worker. I like him.

"Hello, Dick," I shouted.

"Hello yourself, Mr. Grayson," he replied.

He hung his scythe in the branches of a pear tree and we both turned into the barnyard to get the chores out of the way. I wanted to delay the cutting as long as I could — until the dew on the clover should begin — at least — to disappear.

By half-past-seven we were ready for work. We rolled back our sleeves, stood our scythes on end and gave them a final lively stoning. You could hear the brisk sound of the ringing metal pealing through the still morning air.

"It's a great day for haying," I said.

"A dang good one," responded the laconic Dick, wetting his thumb to feel the edge of his scythe.

I cannot convey with any mere pen upon any mere paper the feeling of jauntiness I had at that moment, as of conquest and fresh adventure, as of great things to be done in a great world! You may say if you like that this exhilaration was due to good health and the exuberance of youth. But it was more than that — far more. I cannot well express it, but it seemed as though at that moment Dick and I were stepping out into some vast current of human activity: as though we had the universe itself behind us, and the warm regard and approval of all men.

I stuck my whetstone in my hip-pocket, bent forward and cut the first short sharp swath in the clover. I swept the mass of tangled green stems into the open space just outside the gate. Three or four more strokes and Dick stopped whistling suddenly, spat on his hands and with a lively "Here she goes!" came swinging in behind me. The clover-cutting had begun.

At first I thought the heat would be utterly

unendurable, and, then, with dripping face and wet shoulders, I forgot all about it. Oh, there is something incomparable about such work — the long steady pull of willing and healthy muscles, the mind undisturbed by any disquieting thought, the feeling of attainment through vigorous effort! It was a steady swing and swish, swish and swing! When Dick led I have a picture of him in my mind's eye — his wiry thin legs, one heel lifted at each step and held rigid for a single instant, a glimpse of pale blue socks above his rusty shoes and three inches of whetstone sticking from his tight hip-pocket. It was good to have him there whether he led or followed.

At each return to the orchard end of the field we looked for and found a gray stone jug in the grass. I had brought it up with me filled with cool water from the pump. Dick had a way of swinging it up with one hand, resting it in his shoulder, turning his head just so and letting the water gurgle into his throat. I have never been able myself to reach this refinement in the art of drinking from a jug.

And oh! the good feel of a straightened

back after two long swathes in the broiling sun! We would stand a moment in the shade, whetting our scythes, not saying much, but glad to be there together. Then we would go at it again with renewed energy. It is a great thing to have a working companion. Many times that day Dick and I looked aside at each other with a curious sense of friendliness — that sense of friendliness which grows out of common rivalries, common difficulties and a common weariness. We did not talk much: and that little of trivial matters.

"Jim Brewster's mare had a colt on Wednesday."

"This'll go three tons to the acre, or I'll eat my shirt."

Dick was always about to eat his shirt if some particular prophecy of his did not materialize.

"Dang it all," says Dick, "the moon's drawin' water."

"Something is undoubtedly drawing it," said I, wiping my dripping face.

A meadow lark sprang up with a song in the adjoining field, a few heavy old bumblebees droned in the clover as we cut it, and once a frightened rabbit ran out, darting swiftly under the orchard fence.

So the long forenoon slipped away. At times it seemed endless, and yet we were surprised when we heard the bell from the house (what a sound it was!) and we left our cutting in the middle of the field, nor waited for another stroke.

"Hungry, Dick?" I asked.

"Hungry!" exclaimed Dick with all the eloquence of a lengthy oration crowded into one word.

So we drifted through the orchard, and it was good to see the house with smoke in the kitchen chimney, and the shade of the big maple where it rested upon the porch. And not far from the maple we could see our friendly pump with the moist boards of the well-cover in front of it. I cannot tell you how good it looked as we came in from the hot, dry fields.

"After you," says Dick.

I gave my sleeves another roll upward and unbuttoned and turned in the moist collar of my shirt. Then I stooped over and put my head under the pump spout.

"Pump, Dick," said I.

And Dick pumped.

"Harder, Dick," said I in a strangled voice.

And Dick pumped still harder, and presently I came up gasping with my head and hair dripping with the cool water. Then I pumped for Dick.

"Gee, but that's good," says Dick.

Harriet came out with clean towels, and we dried ourselves, and talked together in low voices. And feeling a delicious sense of coolness we sat down for a moment in the shade of the maple and rested our arms on our knees. From the kitchen, as we sat there, we could hear the engaging sounds of preparation, and busy voices, and the tinkling of dishes, and agreeable odours! Ah, friend and brother, there may not be better moments in life than this!

So we sat resting, thinking of nothing; and presently we heard the screen door click and Ann Spencer's motherly voice:

'Come in now, Mr. Grayson, and get your dinner."

Harriet had set the table on the east porch, where it was cool and shady. Dick and I sat down opposite each other and between us there was a great brown bowl of moist brown beans with crispy strips of pork on top, and a good steam rising from its depths; and a small mountain of baked potatoes, each a little broken to show the snowy white interior; and two towers of such new bread as no one on this earth (or in any other planet so far as I know) but Harriet can make. And before we had even begun our dinner in came the ample Ann Spencer, quaking with hospitality, and bearing a platter — let me here speak of it with the bated breath of a proper respect, for I cannot even now think of it without a sort of inner thrill — bearing a platter of her most famous fried chicken. Harriet had sacrificed the promising careers of two young roosters upon the altar of this important occasion. I may say in passing that Ann Spencer is more celebrated in our neighbourhood by virtue of her genius at frying chicken, than Aristotle or Solomon or Socrates, or indeed all the big-wigs of the past rolled into one.

So we fell to with a silent but none the less fervid enthusiasm. Harriet hovered about us, in and out of the kitchen, and poured the tea and the buttermilk, and Ann Spencer upon every possible occasion passed the chicken.

"More chicken, Mr. Grayson?" she would inquire in a tone of voice that made your mouth water.

"More chicken, Dick?" I'd ask.

"More chicken, Mr. Grayson," he would respond — and thus we kept up a tenuous, but pleasant little joke between us.

Just outside the porch in a thicket of lilacs a catbird sang to us while we ate, and my dog lay in the shade with his nose on his paws and one eye open just enough to show any stray flies that he was not to be trifled with — and far away to the North and East one could catch glimpses — if he had eyes for such things — of the wide-stretching pleasantness of our countryside.

I soon saw that something mysterious was going on in the kitchen. Harriet would look significantly at Ann Spencer and Ann Spencer, who could scarcely contain her overflowing smiles, would look significantly at Harriet. As for me, I sat there with perfect confidence in myself — in my ultimate capacity, as it were. Whatever happened, I was ready for it!

And the great surprise came at last: a SHORT-CAKE: a great, big, red, juicy, buttery, sugary short-cake, with raspberries heaped up all over it. When It came in — and I am speaking of it in that personal way because it radiated such an effulgence that I cannot now remember whether it was Harriet or Ann Spencer who brought it in — when It came in, Dick, who pretends to be abashed upon such occasions, gave one swift glance upward and then emitted a long, low, expressive whistle. When Beethoven found himself throbbing with undescribable emotions he composed a sonata; when Keats felt odd things stirring within him he wrote an ode to an urn, but my friend Dick, quite as evidently on fire with his emotions, merely whistled — and then looked around evidently embarrassed lest he should have infringed upon the proprieties of that occasion.

"Harriet," I said, "you and Ann Spencer are benefactors of the human race."

"Go 'way now," said Ann Spencer, shaking all over with pleasure, "and eat your short-cake."

And after dinner how pleasant it was to

stretch at full length for a few minutes on the grass in the shade of the maple tree and look up through the dusky thick shadows of the leaves. If ever a man feels the blissfulness of complete content it is at such a moment — every muscle in the body deliciously resting, and a peculiar exhilaration animating the mind to quiet thoughts. I have heard talk of the hard work of the hay-fields, but I never yet knew a healthy man who did not recall many moments of exquisite pleasure connected with the hardest and the hottest work.

I think sometimes that the nearer a man can place himself in the full current of natural things the happier he is. If he can become a part of the Universal Process and know that he is a part, that is happiness. All day yesterday I had that deep quiet feeling that I was somehow not working for myself, not because I was covetous for money, nor driven by fear, not surely for fame, but somehow that I was a necessary element in the processes of the earth. I was a primal force! I was the indispensable Harvester. Without me the earth could not revolve!

Oh, friend, there are spiritual values here,

too. For how can a man know God without yielding himself fully to the processes of God?

I *lived* yesterday. I played my part. I took my place. And all hard things grew simple, and all crooked things seemed straight, and all roads were open and clear before me. Many times that day I paused and looked up from my work knowing that I had something to be happy for.

At one o'clock Dick and I lagged our way unwillingly out to work again — rusty of muscles, with a feeling that the heat would now surely be unendurable and the work impossibly hard. The scythes were oddly heavy and hot to the touch, and the stones seemed hardly to make a sound in the heavy noon air. The cows had sought the shady pasture edges, the birds were still, all the air shook with heat. Only man must toil!

"It's danged hot," said Dick conclusively.

How reluctantly we began the work and how difficult it seemed compared with the task of the morning! In half an hour, however, the reluctance passed away and we were swinging as steadily as we did at any time in the forenoon. But we said less — if that were possible — and made every ounce of energy count. I shall not here attempt to chronicle all the events of the afternoon, how we finished the mowing of the field and how we went over it swiftly and raked the long windrows into cocks, or how, as the evening began to fall, we turned at last wearily toward the house. The day's work was done.

Dick had stopped whistling long before the middle of the afternoon, but now as he shouldered his scythe he struck up "My Fairy Fay" with some marks of his earlier enthusiasm.

"Well, Dick," said I, "we've had a good day's work together."

"You bet," said Dick.

And I watched him as he went down the lane with a pleasant friendly feeling of companionship. We had done great things together.

I wonder if you ever felt the joy of utter physical weariness: not exhaustion, but weariness. I wonder if you have ever sat down, as I did last night, and felt as though you would like to remain just there always — without stirring a single muscle, without speaking, without thinking even!

Such a moment is not painful, but quite the reverse — it is supremely pleasant. So I sat for a time last evening on my porch. The cool, still night had fallen sweetly after the burning heat of the day. I heard all the familiar sounds of the night. A whippoorwill began to whistle in the distant thicket. Harriet came out quietly — I could see the white of her gown — and sat near me. I heard the occasional sleepy tinkle of a cowbell, and the crickets were calling. A star or two came out in the perfect dark blue of the sky. The deep, sweet, restful night was on. I don't know that I said it aloud — such things need not be said aloud — but as I turned almost numbly into the house, stumbling on my way to bed, my whole being seemed to cry out: "Thank God, thank God."

AN OLD MAN

XI

AN OLD MAN

TO-DAY I saw Uncle Richard Summers walking in the town road: and cannot get him out of my mind. I think I never knew any one who wears so plainly the garment of Detached Old Age as he. One would not now think of calling him a farmer, any more than one would think of calling him a doctor, or a lawyer, or a justice of the peace. No one would think now of calling him "Squire Summers," though he bore that name with no small credit many years ago. He is no longer known as hard-working, or able, or grasping, or rich, or wicked: he is just Old. Everything seems to have been stripped away from Uncle Richard except age.

How well I remember the first time Uncle Richard Summers impressed himself upon my mind. It was after the funeral of his old wife, now several years ago. I saw him standing at the open grave with his broad-brimmed felt hat held at his breast. His head was bowed and his thin, soft, white hair stirred in the warm breeze. I wondered at his quietude. After fifty years or more together his nearest companion and friend had gone, and he did not weep aloud. Afterward I was again impressed with the same fortitude or quietude. I saw him walking down the long drive to the main road with all the friends of our neighbourhood about him — and the trees rising full and calm on one side, and the still greenery of the cemetery stretching away on the other. Half way down the drive he turned aside to the fence and all unconscious of the halted procession, he picked a handful of the large leaves of the wild grape. It was a hot day; he took off his hat, and put the cool leaves in the crown of it and rejoined the procession. It did not seem to me to be the mere forgetfulness of old age, nor yet callousness to his own great sorrow. It was rather an instinctive return to the immeasureable continuity of the trivial things of life — the trivial necessary things which so often carry us over the greatest tragedies.

I talked with the Scotch Preacher afterward about the incident. He said that he, too, marveling at the old man's calmness, had referred to it in his presence. Uncle Richard turned to him and said slowly:

"I am an old man, and I have learned one thing. I have learned to accept life."

Since that day I have seen Uncle Richard Summers many times walking on the country roads with his cane. He always looks around at me and slowly nods his head, but rarely says anything. At his age what is there to say that has not already been said?

His trousers appear a size too large for him, his hat sets too far down, his hands are long and thin upon the head of his cane. But his face is tranquil. He has come a long way; there have been times of tempest and keen winds, there have been wild hills in his road, and rocky places, and threatening voices in the air. All that is past now: and his face is tranquil.

I think we younger people do not often

realize how keenly dependent we are upon our contemporaries in age. We get little understanding and sympathy either above or below them. Much of the world is a little misty to us, a little out of focus. Uncle Richard Summers's contemporaries have nearly all gone — mostly long ago: one of the last, his old wife. At his home — I have been there often to see his son — he sits in a large rocking chair with a cushion in it, and a comfortable high back to lean upon. No one else ventures to sit in his chair, even when he is not there. It is not far from the window; and when he sits down he can lean his cane against the wall where he can easily reach it again.

There is a turmoil of youth and life always about him; of fevered incomings and excited outgoings, of work and laughter and tears and joy and anger. He watches it all, for his mind is still clear, but he does not take sides. He accepts everything, refuses nothing; or, if you like, he refuses everything, accepts nothing.

He once owned the house where he now lives, with the great barns behind it and the fertile acres spreading far on every hand.

From his chair he can look out through a small window, and see the sun on the quiet fields. He once went out swiftly and strongly, he worked hotly, he came in wearied to sleep.

Now he lives in a small room — and that is more than is really necessary — and when he walks out he does not inquire who owns the land where he treads. He lets the hot world go by, and waits with patience the logic of events.

Often as I have passed him in the road, I have wondered, as I have been wondering to-day, how he must look out upon us all, upon our excited comings and goings, our immense concern over the immeasurably trivial. I have wondered, not without a pang, and a resolution, whether I shall ever reach the point where I can let this eager and fascinating world go by without taking toll of it!

THE CELEBRITY

XII

THE CELEBRITY

NOT for many weeks have I had a more interesting, more illuminating, and when all is told, a more amusing experience, than I had this afternoon. Since this afternoon the world has seemed a more satisfactory place to live in, and my own home here, the most satisfactory, the most central place in all the world. I have come to the conclusion that anything may happen here!

We have had a celebrity in our small midst, and the hills, as the Psalmist might say, have lifted up their heads, and the trees have clapped their hands together. He came here last Tuesday evening and spoke at the School House. I was not there myself; if I had been, I should not, perhaps, have had the adventure which has made this day so livable, nor met the Celebrity face to face.

Let me here set down a close secret regarding celebrities:

They cannot survive without common people like you and me.

It follows that if we do not pursue a celebrity, sooner or later he will pursue us. He must; it is the law of his being. So I wait here very comfortably on my farm, and as I work in my fields I glance up casually from time to time to see if any celebrities are by chance coming up the town road to seek me out. Oh, we are crusty people, we farmers! Sooner or later they all come this way, all the warriors and the poets, all the philosophers and the prophets and the politicians. If they do not, indeed, get time to come before they are dead, we have full assurance that they will straggle along afterward clad neatly in sheepskin, or more gorgeously in green buckram with gilt lettering. Whatever the airs of pompous importance they may assume as they come, back of it all we farmers can see the look of wistful eagerness in their eyes. They know well enough that they must give us something which we in our commonness regard as valuable enough to exchange for a bushel of our potatoes, or a sack of our white onions. No poem that we can enjoy, no speech that tickles us, no prophecy that thrills us — neither dinner nor immortality for them! And we are hard-headed Yankees at our bargainings; many a puffed-up celebrity loses his puffiness at our doors!

This afternoon, as I came out on my porch after dinner, feeling content with myself and all the world, I saw a man driving our way in a one-horse top-buggy. In the country it is our custom first to identify the horse, and that gives us a sure clue to the identification of the driver. This horse plainly did not belong in our neighbourhood and plainly as it drew nearer, it bore the unmistakable marks of the town livery. Therefore, the driver, in all probability, was a stranger in these parts. What strangers were in town who would wish to drive this way? The man who occupied the buggy was large and slow-looking; he wore a black, broad-brimmed felt hat and a black coat, a man evidently of some presence. And he drove slowly and awkwardly; not an agent plainly. Thus the logic of the country bore fruitage.

"Harriet," I said, calling through the open doorway, "I think the Honourable Arthur Caldwell is coming here."

"Mercy me!" exclaimed Harriet, appearing in the doorway, and as quickly disappearing. I did not see her, of course, but I knew instinctively that she was slipping off her apron, moving our most celebrated rocking-chair two inches nearer the door, and whisking a few invisible particles of dust from the centre table. Every time any one of importance comes our way, or is distantly likely to come our way, Harriet resolves herself into an amiable whirlwind of good order, subsiding into placidity at the first sound of a step on the porch.

As for me I remain in my shirt sleeves, sitting on my porch resting a moment after my dinner. No sir, I will positively not go in and get my coat. I am an American citizen, at home in my house with the sceptre of my dominion — my favourite daily newspaper — in my hand. Let all kings, queens, and other potentates approach!

And besides, though I am really much afraid that the Honourable Arthur Caldwell will not stop at my gate but will pass on toward Horace's, I am nursing a somewhat light opinion of Mr. Caldwell. When he spoke at the School House on Tuesday, I did not go to hear him, nor was my opinion greatly changed by what I learned afterward of the meeting. I take both of our weekly county papers. This is necessary. I add the news of both together, divide by two to strike a fair average, and then ask Horace, or Charles Baxter, or the Scotch Preacher what really happened. The Republican county paper said of the meeting:

"The Honourable Arthur Caldwell, member of Congress, who is seeking a reëlection, was accorded a most enthusiastic reception by a large and sympathetic audience of the citizens of Blandford township on Tuesday evening."

Strangely enough the Democratic paper,

observing exactly the same historic events, took this jaundiced view of the matter:

"Arty Caldwell, Republican boss of the Sixth District, who is out mending his political fences, spellbound a handful of his henchmen at the School House near Blandford Crossing on Tuesday evening."

And here was Mr. Caldwell himself, Member of Congress, Leader of the Sixth District, Favourably Mentioned for Governor, drawing up at my gate, deliberately descending from his buggy, with dignity stopping to take the tie-rein from under the seat, carefully tying his horse to my hitching-post.

I confess I could not help feeling a thrill of excitement. Here was a veritable Celebrity come to my house to explain himself! I would not have it known, of course, outside of our select circle of friends, but I confess that although I am a pretty independent person (when I talk) in reality there are few things in this world I would rather see than a new person coming up the walk to my door. We cannot, of course, let the celebrities know it, lest they grow intolerable in their toploftiness, but if they must have us, we cannot well get along without them — without the colour and variety which they lend to a gray world. I have spent many a precious moment alone in my fields looking up the road (with what wistful casualness!) for some new Socrates or Mark Twain, and I have not been wholly disappointed when I have had to content myself with the Travelling Evangelist or the Syrian Woman who comes this way monthly bearing her pack of cheap suspenders and blue bandana handkerchiefs.

"Good afternoon, Mr. Grayson," said the Honourable Mr. Caldwell, taking off his large hat and pausing with one foot on my step.

"Good afternoon, sir," I responded, "won't you come up?"

He sat down in the chair opposite me with a certain measured and altogether impressive dignity. I cannot say that he was exactly condescending in his manners, yet he made me feel that it was no small honour to have so considerable a person sitting there on the porch with me. At the same time he was outwardly not without a sort of patient deference which was evidently calculated to put me at my ease. Oh, he had all the arts of the schooled politician! He knew to the last shading just the attitude that he as a great man, a leader in Congress, a dominant force in his party, a possible candidate for Governor (and yet always a seeker for the votes of the people!) must observe in approaching a free farmer — like me — sitting at ease in his shirt-sleeves on his own porch, taking a moment's rest after dinner. It was a perfect thing to see!

He had evidently heard, what was not altogether true, that I was a questioner of authority, a disturber of the political peace, and that (concretely) I was opposing him for reëlection. And it was as plain as a pikestaff that he was here to lay down the political law to me. He would do it smilingly and patiently, but firmly. He would use all the leverage of his place, his power, his personal appearance, to crush the presumptuous uprising against his authority.

I confess my spirits rose at the thought. What in this world is more enthralling than the meeting of an unknown adversary upon the open field, and jousting him a tourney. I felt like some modern Robin Hood facing the panoplied authority of the King's man.

And what a place and time it was for a

combat — in the quietude of the summer afternoon, no sound anywhere breaking the still warmth and sweetness except the buzzing of bees in the clematis at the end of the porch — and all about the green countryside, woods and fields and old fences — and the brown road leading its venturesome way across a distant hill toward the town.

After explaining who he was — I told him I had recognized him on sight — we opened with a volley of small shot. We peppered one another with harmless comments on the weather and the state of the crops. He advanced cabbages and I countered with sugar-beets. I am quite aware that there are good tacticians who deprecate the use of skirmish lines and the desultory fire of the musketry of small talk. They would advance in grim silence and open at once with the crushing fire of their biggest guns.

But such fighting is not for me. I should lose half the joy of the battle, and kill off my adversary before I had begun to like him! It wouldn't do, it wouldn't do at all.

"It's a warm day," observes my opponent, and I take a sure measure of his fighting form. I rather like the look of his eye.

"I never saw the corn ripening better," I observe, and let him feel a little of the cunning of the arrangement of my forces.

There is much in the tone of the voice, the cut of the words, the turn of a phrase. I can be your servant with a "Yes sir," or your master with a "No sir."

Thus we warm up to one another — a little at a time — we mass our forces, each sees the white of his adversary's eyes. I can even see my opponent — with some joy — trotting up his reserves, having found the opposition stronger than he at first supposed.

"I hear," said Mr. Caldwell, finally, with a smile intended to be disarming, "that you are opposing my reëlection."

Boom! the cannon's opening roar!

"Well," I replied, also smiling, and not to be outdone in the directness of my thrust, "I have told a few of my friends that I thought Mr. Gaylord would represent us better in Congress than you have done."

Boom! the fight is on!

"You are a Republican, aren't you, Mr. Grayson?"

It was the inevitable next stroke. When he found that I was a doubtful follower of him personally, he marshalled the Authority of the Institution which he represented.

"I have voted the Republican ticket," I said, "but I confess that recently I have not been able to distinguish Republicans from Democrats — and I've had my doubts," said I, "whether there is any real Republican party left to vote with."

I cannot well describe the expression on his face, nor indeed, now that the battle was on, horsemen, footmen, and big guns, shall I attempt to chronicle every stroke and counter-stroke of that great conflict.

This much is certain: there was something universal and primal about the battle waged this quiet afternoon on my porch between Mr. Caldwell and me; it was the primal struggle between the leader and the follower; between the representative and the represented. And it is a never-ending conflict. When the leader gains a small advantage the pendulum of civilization swings toward aristocracy; and when the follower, beginning to think, beginning to struggle, gains a small advantage, then the pendulum inclines toward democracy.

And always, and always, the leaders tend

to forget that they are only servants, and would be masters. "The unending audacity of elected persons!" And always, and always, there must be a following bold enough to prick the pretensions of the leaders and keep them in their places!

Thus, through the long still afternoon, the battle waged upon my porch. Harriet came out and met the Honourable Mr. Caldwell, and sat and listened, and presently went in again, without having got half a dozen words into the conversation. And the bees buzzed, and in the meadows the cows began to come out of the shade to feed in the open land.

Gradually, Mr. Caldwell put off his air of condescension; he put off his appeal to party authority; he even stopped arguing the tariff and the railroad question. Gradually, he ceased to be the great man, Favourably Mentioned for Governor, and came down on the ground with me. He moved his chair up closer to mine; he put his hand on my knee. For the first time I began to see what manner of man he was: to find out how much real fight he had in him.

"You don't understand," he said, "what it means to be down there at Washington

"HE MOVED HIS CHAIR CLOSER TO MINE"

in a time like this. Things clear to you are not clear when you have to meet men in the committees and on the floor of the house who have a contrary view from yours and hold to it just as tenaciously as you do to your views."

Well, sir, he gave me quite a new impression of what a Congressman's job was like, of what difficulties and dissensions he had to meet at home, and what compromises he had to accept when he reached Washington.

"Do you know," I said to him, with some enthusiasm, "I am more than ever convinced that farming is good enough for me."

He threw back his head and laughed uproariously, and then moved up still closer.

"The trouble with you, Mr. Grayson," he said, "is that you are looking for a giant intellect to represent you at Washington."

"Yes," I said, "I'm afraid I am."

"Well," he returned, "they don't happen along every day. I'd like to see the House of Representatives full of Washingtons and Jeffersons and Websters and Roosevelts. But there's a Lincoln only once in a century."

He paused and then added with a sort of wry smile:

"And any quantity of Caldwells!"

That took me! I liked him for it. It was so explanatory. The armour of political artifice, the symbols of political power, had now all dropped away from him, and we sat there together, two plain and friendly human beings, arriving through stress and struggle at a common understanding. He was not a great leader, not a statesman at all, but plainly a man of determination, with a fair measure of intelligence and sincerity. He had a human desire to stay in Congress, for the life evidently pleased him, and while he would never be crucified as a prophet, I felt — what I had not felt before in regard to him — that he was sincerely anxious to serve the best interests of his constituents. Added to these qualities he was a man who was loyal to his friends; and not ungenerous to his enemies.

Up to this time he had done most of the talking; but now, having reached a common basis, I leaned forward with some eagerness.

"You won't mind," I said, "if I give you my view — my common country view of the political situation. I am sure I don't understand, and I don't think my neighbours here understand, much about the tariff or the trusts or the railroad question — in detail. We get general impressions — and stick to them like grim death — for we know somehow that we are right. Generally speaking, we here in the country work for what we get ——"

"And sometimes put the big apples at the top of the barrel," nodded Mr. Caldwell.

"And sometimes put too much salt on top of the butter," I added — "all that, but on the whole we get only what we earn by the hard daily work of ploughing and planting and reaping: You admit that."

"I admit it," said Mr. Caldwell.

"And we've got the impression that a good many of the men down in New York and Boston, and elsewhere, through the advantages which the tariff laws, and other laws, are giving them, are getting more than they earn — a lot more. And we feel that laws must be passed which will prevent all that."

"Now, I believe that, too," said Mr. Caldwell very earnestly.

"Then we belong to the same party," I said. "I don't know what the name of it is yet, but we both belong to it."

Mr. Caldwell laughed.

"And I'll appoint you," I said "my agent in Washington to work out the changes in the laws."

"Well, I'll accept the appointment," said Mr. Caldwell — continuing very earnestly, "if you'll trust to my honesty and not expect too much of me all at once."

With that we both sat back in our chairs and looked at each other and laughed with the greatest good humour and common understanding.

"And now," said I, rising quickly, "let's go and get a drink of buttermilk."

So we walked around the house arm in arm and stopped in the shade of the oak tree which stands near the spring-house. Harriet came out in the whitest of white dresses, carrying a tray with the glasses, and I opened the door of the spring-house, and felt the cool air on my face and smelt the good smell of butter and milk and cottage cheese, and I passed the cool pitcher to Harriet. And so we drank together there in the shade and talked and laughed.

I walked down with Mr. Caldwell to the gate. He took my arm and said to me:

"I'm glad I came out here and had this

talk. I feel as though I understood my job better for it."

"Let's organize a new party," I said, "let's begin with two members, you and I, and have only one plank in the platform."

He smiled.

"You'd have to crowd a good deal into that one plank," he said.

"Not at all," I responded.

"What would you have it?"

"I'd have it in one sentence," I said, "and something like this: We believe in the passage of legislation which shall prevent any man taking from the common store any more than he actually earns."

Mr. Caldwell threw up his arms.

"Mr. Grayson," he said, "you're an outrageous idealist."

"Mr. Caldwell," I said, "you'll say one of these days that I'm a practical politician."

"Well, Harriet," I said, "he's got my vote."

"Well, David," said Harriet, "that's what he came for."

"It's an interesting world, Harriet," I said.

"It is, indeed," said Harriet.

As we stood on the porch we could see at the top of the hill, where the town road crosses it, the slow moving buggy, and through the open curtain at the back the heavy form of our Congressman with his slouch hat set firmly on his big head.

"We may be fooled, Harriet," I observed, "on dogmas and doctrines and platforms — but if we cannot trust human nature in the long run, what hope is there? It's men we must work with, Harriet."

"And women," said Harriet.

"And women, of course," said I.

ON FRIENDSHIP

XIII

ON FRIENDSHIP

I COME now to the last of these Adventures in Friendship. As I go out — I hope not for long — I wish you might follow me to the door, and then as we continue to talk quietly, I may beguile you, all unconsciously, to the top of the steps, or even find you at my side when we reach the gate at the end of the lane. I wish you might hate to let me go, as I myself hate to go! — And when I reach the top of the hill (if you wait long enough) you will see me turn and wave my hand; and you will know that I am still relishing the joy of our meeting, and that I part unwillingly.

Not long ago, a friend of mine wrote a letter asking me an absurdly difficult question — difficult because so direct and simple.

"What is friendship, anyway?" queried this philosophical correspondent.

The truth is, the question came to me with a shock, as something quite new. For I have spent so much time thinking of my friends that I have scarcely ever stopped to reflect upon the abstract quality of friendship. My attention being thus called to the subject, I fell to thinking of it the other night as I sat by the fire, Harriet not far away rocking and sewing, and my dog sleeping on the rug near me (his tail stirring whenever I made a motion to leave my place). And whether I would or no my friends came trooping into my mind. I thought of our neighbour Horace, the dryly practical and sufficient farmer, and of our much loved Scotch Preacher; I thought of the Shy Bee-man and of his boisterous double, the Bold Bee-man; I thought of the Old Maid, and how she talks, for all the world like a rabbit running in a furrow (all on the same line until you startle her out, when she slips quickly into the next furrow and goes on running as ardently as before). And I thought of John Starkweather, our rich man; and of the life of the girl Anna. And it was good to think of them all living around me, not far away, connected with me through darkness and space by a certain mysterious human cord. (Oh, there are mysteries still left upon this scientific earth!) As I sat there by the fire I told them over one by one, remembering with warmth or amusement or concern this or that characteristic thing about each of them. It was the next best thing to hearing the tramp of feet on my porch, to seeing the door fly open (letting in a gust of the fresh cool air!), to crying a hearty greeting, to drawing up an easy chair to the open fire, to watching with eagerness while my friend unwraps (exclaiming all the while of the state of the weather: "Cold, Grayson, mighty cold!") and finally sits down beside me, not too far away.

The truth is, — my philosophical correspondent — I cannot formulate any theory of friendship which will cover all the conditions. I know a few things that friendship is not, and a few things that it is, but when I come to generalize upon the abstract quality I am quite at a loss for adequate language.

Friendship, it seems to me, is like happiness. She flies pursuit, she is shy, and wild, and timid, and will be best wooed by indirection. Quite unexpectedly, sometimes, as we pass in the open road, she puts her hand in ours, like a child. Friendship is neither a formality nor a mode: it is rather a life. Many and many a time I have seen Charles Baxter at work in his carpentry-shop — just working, or talking in his quiet voice, or looking around occasionally through his steel-bowed spectacles, and I have had the feeling that I should like to go over and sit on the bench near him. He literally talks me over! I even want to touch him!

It is not the substance of what we say to one another that makes us friends, nor yet the manner of saying it, nor is it what you do or I do, nor is it what I give you, or you give me, nor is it because we chance to belong to the same church, or society or party that makes us friendly. Nor is it because we entertain the same views or respond to the same emotions. All these things may serve to bring us nearer together but no one of them can of itself kindle the divine fire of friendship. A friend is one with whom we are fond of being when no business is afoot nor any entertainment contemplated. A man may well be silent with a friend. "I do not need to ask the wounded person how he feels," says the poet, "I myself became the wounded person."

Not all people come to friendship in the same way. Some possess a veritable genius for intimacy and will be making a dozen friends where I make one. Our Scotch Preacher is such a person. I never knew any man with a gift of intimacy so persuasive as his. He is so simple and direct that he cuts through the stoniest reserve and strikes at once upon those personal things which with all of us are so far more real than any outward interest. "Good-morning, friend," I have heard him say to a total stranger, and within half an hour they had their heads together and were talking of things which make men cry. It is an extraordinary gift.

As for me, I confess it to be a selfish interest or curiosity which causes me to stop almost any man by the way, and to take something of what he has — because it pleases me to do so. I try to pay in coin as good as I get, but I recognize it as a lawless procedure. For the coin I give (being such as I myself secretly make) is for them sometimes only spurious metal, while what I get is for me the very treasure of the Indies. For a lift in my wagon, a drink at the door, a flying word across my fences, I have taken argosies of minted wealth!

Especially do I enjoy all travelling people. I wait for them (how eagerly) here on my farm. I watch the world drift by in daily tides upon the road, flowing outward in the morning toward the town, and as surely at evening drifting back again. I look out with a pleasure impossible to convey upon those who come this way from the town: the Syrian woman going by in the gray town road, with her bright-coloured head-dress, and her oil-cloth pack; and the Old-ironman with his dusty wagon, jangling his little bells, and the cheerful weazened Herb-doctor in his faded hat, and the Signman with his mouth full of nails — how they are all marked upon by the town, all dusted with the rosy bloom of human experience. How often in fancy I have pursued them down the valley and watched them until they drifted out of sight beyond the hill! Or how often I have stopped them or they (too willingly) have stopped me — and we have fenced and parried with fine bold words.

If you should ever come by my farm — you, whoever you are — take care lest I board you, hoist my pirate flag, and sail you away to the Enchanted Isle where I make my rendezvous.

It is not short of miraculous how, with cultivation, one's capacity for friendship increases. Once I myself had scarcely room in my heart for a single friend, who am now so wealthy in friendships. It is a phenomenon worthy of consideration by all hardened disbelievers in that which is miraculous upon this earth that when a man's heart really opens to a friend he finds there room for two. And when he takes in the second, behold the skies lift, and the earth grows wider, and he finds there room for two more!

In a curious passage (which I understand

no longer darkly) old mystical Swedenborg tells of his wonderment that the world of spirits (which he says he visited so familiarly) should not soon become too small for all the swelling hosts of its ethereal inhabitants, and was confronted with the discovery that the more angels there were, the more heaven to hold them!

So let it be with our friendships!

THE END